JOHNSON

HISTORY OF RASSELAS

PRINCE OF ABYSSINIA

EDITED

WITH INTRODUCTION AND NOTES

BY

GEORGE BIRKBECK HILL, D.C.L., LL.D.

HONORARY FELLOW OF PEMBROKE COLLEGE, OXFORD

OXFORD

AT THE CLARENDON PRESS

Oxford University Press, Amen House, London E.C.4

GLASGOW NEW YORK TORONTO MELBOURNE WELLINGTON
BOMBAY CALCUTTA MADRAS KARACHI KUALA LUMPUR
CAPE TOWN IBADAN NAIROBI ACCRA

IMPRESSION OF 1958
FIRST EDITION 1887

PRINTED IN GREAT BRITAIN

CONTENTS.

INTRODUCTION.

SAMUEL JOHNSON was born on September 18, 1709, in the old house that still stands at the corner of the market-place in Lichfield, and died on December 13, 1784, in Bolt Court, Fleet Street. The birth of the son of a small country bookseller passed unnoticed, but 'his death,' said a popular writer of his time, 'makes a kind of era in literature [1].' In one, and in one thing only, did fortune favour him. He was bred in the midst of books, for he had the run of his father's shop. One day he climbed up to a shelf in search of some apples which he imagined that his brother had hidden behind a large folio. 'There were no apples; but the large folio proved to be Petrarch, whom he had seen mentioned in some preface as one of the restorers of learning. His curiosity having been thus excited, he sat down with avidity, and read a great part of the book [2].' So widely did he read that when he entered Pembroke College, Oxford, his tutor told him 'he was the best qualified for the University that he had ever known come there [3].' He had almost everything against him. His life was too much like Pope's, one 'long disease [4].' Scrofula had disfigured his face, and deprived him of the use of one eye. He was subject to 'convulsive starts, and odd gesticulations, which tended to excite at once surprise and ridicule [5].' He was often troubled with a melancholy, which at one time was only divided by a thin partition

---

[1] Hannah More, *Memoirs*, i. 394.
[2] Boswell's *Life of Johnson*, Clarendon Press ed., i. 57.   [3] *Ib.*
[4] 'This long disease, my life.'—*Prologues to the Satires*, l. 132.
[5] Boswell's *Life of Johnson*, i. 95.

from madness [1]. In his old age he said that his health from his twentieth year had been such as seldom afforded him a day of ease [2]. On the other hand, he possessed great bodily strength, a mind that was capable of extraordinary effort, and that worked with uncommon rapidity, and a happy facility of forgetting his troubles in the long hours which he gave to the society of his friends.

Till he received his pension, in his fifty-third year, he had had a never-ceasing struggle with poverty. His father found indeed the means to send him to the University, but could not afford to keep him there long. After a residence of fourteen months ' poor Samuel Johnson returned to his native city, destitute, and not knowing how he should gain even a decent livelihood [3].' In the present happier days, when scholarships are open to all, the youth who could turn Pope's *Messiah* into such Latin verse as Johnson turned it would never be driven by poverty from a wealthy University. By his father's death, which soon followed, Johnson was now forced to seek his livelihood. He tried a place as an usher in a grammar-school; but schools at this time were far too often dens of misery both for undermasters and boys. After a few months ' he relinquished a situation which all his life long he recollected with the strongest aversion, and even a degree of horror [4].' He sought the post of head-master, but was unsuccessful, on one occasion because he did not possess the degree of Master of Arts, and on another, because, to quote an old letter which still exists, ' he has the caracter of being a very haughty, ill-natured gent., and y[t] he has such a way of distorting his Face (which though he can't help) y[e] gent. think it may affect some young ladds [5].' He sought work as an author, and vainly published proposals for printing the Latin Poems of Politian. He was little more successful in his next attempt. He translated from the French Lobo's Voyage to Abyssinia, and receiving for it five

---

[1] Boswell's *Life of Johnson*, i. 276, *n.* 2 ; 521.   [2] *Ib.* iv. 147.
[3] *Ib.* i. 79.   [4] *Ib.* i. 85.   [5] *Ib.* vi. xliv.

guineas was paid at the rate of not quite threepence-farthing a page.

In his twenty-sixth year he married a widow who was full twenty years older than himself. ' To her he proved a most affectionate and indulgent husband to the last moment of her life [1].' With the help of the small fortune that she had [2], he opened a school at Edial, near Lichfield. We may smile at an ' Academy ' which was attended, it is said, by only three pupils in all. Yet what school is there in England that would not be proud, if it could point on its rolls to the name of Samuel Johnson among its masters and David Garrick among its boys ? He soon gave up his school, and with a half-finished tragedy in his pocket came up to London. His travelling-companion was Garrick. He got employment as a writer on the *Gentleman's Magazine*, which was then in the first years of its long existence. For it he wrote short poems, reviews, essays, biographies of eminent men, and his Parliamentary debates. Of these speeches, though they were put in the mouths of members of both Houses, the form was always his, and very often the substance too. His tragedy of *Irene*, though Garrick acted in it, met with slight success. It has never since been put on the stage. Nevertheless it brought its author a sum of money which to him must have seemed considerable. His two poems, *London* and *The Vanity of Human Wishes*, which have stood the judgment of many generations of readers, though their great merits were at once acknowledged, were miserably rewarded. He was paid for them at the rate of about tenpence a line [3]. A single sheet of a paper containing a short letter in his handwriting has within the last few years sold for almost double the sum that he received for these two noble poems [4]. The *Life of Richard Savage* which he wrote about this time gave our country an example of a new kind of biography. The rapidity with which it was

[1] Boswell's *Life of Johnson*, i. 96.   [2] *Ib.* i. 95, *n.* 3.
[3] *Ib.* i 193, *n.* 1.   [4] *Ib.* ii. 297, *n.* 2.

composed was astonishing. 'I wrote,' he said, 'forty-eight of the printed octavo pages at a sitting ; but then I sat up all night [1].' Reynolds, so soon to become famous as a great painter, who did not as yet know its author, ' began to read it while he was standing with his arm leaning against a chimney-piece. It seized his attention so strongly, that not being able to lay down the book till he had finished it, when he attempted to move he found his arm totally benumbed [2].' Johnson soon after projected an edition of Shakespeare, and published as a specimen *Miscellaneous Observations on the Tragedy of Macbeth*. Twenty years however elapsed before he gave this edition to the world.

It was in the year 1747 that he issued his plan or pro-spectus of that which is perhaps the greatest of all his works, his *Dictionary of the English Language*. It was not till the spring of 1755 that it was ready for publication. The plan he had addressed to the Earl of Chesterfield, ' who was at once,' to quote the words of Lord Macaulay, ' the most dis-tinguished orator in the Upper House, and the undisputed sovereign of wit and fashion [3].' By this great nobleman Johnson thought that he was slighted. ' Sir,' said he, ' after making great professions he had for many years taken no notice of me ; but when my *Dictionary* was coming out, he fell a scribbling in *The World* about it.' Chesterfield's scribble was flippant and indecent. Johnson wrote to him that famous letter which is likely to be read as long as the English language is understood [4].

'To the Right Honourable the Earl of
Chesterfield.

February 7, 1755.

My Lord,—I have been lately informed, by the proprietor of the World, that two papers, in which my Dictionary is recommended to the public, were written by your Lordship. To be so distinguished, is an honour, which, being very little

---

[1] Boswell's *Life of Johnson*, i. 166.   [2] *Ib.* i. 165
[3] Trevelyan's *Life of Macaulay*, ed. 1877, i. 325.
[4] Boswell's *Life of Johnson*, i. 259.

accustomed to favours from the great, I know not well how to receive, or in what terms to acknowledge.

When, upon some slight encouragement, I first visited your Lordship, I was overpowered, like the rest of mankind, by the enchantment of your address, and could not forbear to wish that I might boast myself *Le vainqueur du vainqueur de la terre ;*—that I might obtain that regard for which I saw the world contending ; but I found my attendance so little encouraged, that neither pride nor modesty would suffer me to continue it. When I had once addressed your Lordship in public, I had exhausted all the art of pleasing which a retired and uncourtly scholar can possess. I had done all that I could ; and no man is well pleased to have his all neglected, be it ever so little.

Seven years, my Lord, have now passed, since I waited in your outward rooms, or was repulsed from your door ; during which time I have been pushing on my work through diffi-culties, of which it is useless to complain, and have brought it, at last, to the verge of publication, without one act of assistance, one word of encouragement, or one smile of favour. Such treatment I did not expect, for I never had a Patron before.

The shepherd in Virgil[1] grew at last acquainted with Love, and found him a native of the rocks.

Is not a Patron, my Lord, one who looks with unconcern on a man struggling for life in the water, and, when he has reached ground, encumbers him with help ? The notice which you have been pleased to take of my labours, had it been early, had been kind ; but it has been delayed till I am in-different, and cannot enjoy it ; till I am solitary, and cannot impart it ; till I am known, and do not want it. I hope it is no very cynical asperity not to confess obligations where no benefit has been received, or to be unwilling that the Public should consider me as owing that to a Patron, which Provi-dence has enabled me to do for myself.

Having carried on my work thus far with so little obliga-tion to any favourer of learning, I shall not be disappointed though I should conclude it, if less be possible, with less ; for I have been long wakened from that dream of hope, in which I once boasted myself with so much exultation,

MY LORD,

Your lordship's most humble, most obedient servant,

SAM. JOHNSON.'

[1] *Eclogues,* viii. 43.

'While he was bearing his burdens with dull patience, and beating the track of the alphabet with sluggish resolution [1],' he undertook a second task. As if the *Dictionary* were not enough to exhaust his strength, he began a periodical paper. Twice a week, every Tuesday and Saturday, for two years, he published a series of essays under the name of *The Rambler*. Their style did not much please the men of his time, and is generally displeasing to the modern reader. They contain nevertheless much acute criticism, reflections full of wisdom, but too often full of sadness, not a few humorous touches, and many eloquent and even noble passages. The death of his wife followed close on the last number. For forty days he seems to have given himself wholly up to grief ; at their close he used, he records, a service of prayer, ' as preparatory to my return to life to-morrow [2]. He cherished her memory to his last day. Before long he again found time for essay-writing, and contributed many papers to a publication started by his friend, Dr. Hawkesworth, under the name of *The Adventurer*. When his *Dictionary* was on the eve of publication the University of Oxford made some atonement for the neglect it had formerly shown him, and conferred on him the degree of Master of Arts. With this distinction he was highly gratified. He kept back the title-page so that he might grace it with his new honour, and in his frequent visits to Oxford he ' wore his gown almost ostentatiously [3].' Later on he received the degree of Doctor of Laws both from his own university and from Dublin.

An *Abridgment of his Dictionary* next engaged his attention, but he found time as usual for minor pieces of writing. He resumed his project of editing Shakespeare, but so dilatory had he become, perhaps owing to a long strain of excessive labour, that its publication was delayed longer even

---

[1] Johnson's *Works*, ed. 1825, v. 1.
[2] *Prayers and Meditations*, p. 15.
[3] Boswell's *Life of Johnson*, i. 347, *n.* 2.

than that of the Dictionary. During the interval he wrote
a fresh series of essays, to which he gave the name of *The
Idler.* To the death of his mother, which happened at this
time, we owe his admirable story of *Rasselas.* Few tales
have been more widely read. It reached its fifth edition in
less than three years. Johnson lived to see versions in
Italian, French, German, and Dutch. It has since been
translated into Bengalee, Hungarian, Polish, Modern Greek,
Spanish, and Russian [1]. A few years later on, a great and
most happy change was made in his life. Under George II.
he had had no hope of Court favour, for he had openly
avowed his dislike of the House of Hanover. In his heart
he always sided with the Jacobites, though in his reason
he was convinced that the deposition of James II. had
been needful. 'I have heard him declare,' writes Boswell,
'that if holding up his right hand would have secured
victory at Culloden to Prince Charles's army, he was not
sure he would have held it up [2].' The accession of George
III. was soon followed by the return to power of the Tory
party, to which Johnson was strongly attached. He did
nothing however to seek royal favour, and probably no man
was more surprised than he was himself on learning that the
king had been advised by his minister to confer on him
a pension of £300 a year. He was now no longer forced to
write for money, and for fifteen years he wrote very little.
He completed his edition of Shakespeare, revised his *Dictionary*, wrote four political pamphlets which did not raise his
reputation, and his *Journey to the Western Islands*, in which
he describes with force a state of society which was rapidly
passing away. His chief work during all these years was his
talk. He was one of the most accessible of men. He knew
all kinds of people, and was ready to discuss all kinds of
subjects. 'He seemed to me,' as one of his friends said, 'to
be considered as a kind of public oracle, whom everybody
thought they had a right to visit and consult; and doubtless

---

[1] Boswell's *Life of Johnson*, ii. 208; vi. lxiv.   [2] *Ib.* i. 430.

they were well rewarded[1].' It was, as Boswell says, 'in
the art of thinking, the art of using his mind,' that his
superiority chiefly consisted ; 'a certain continual power of
seizing the useful substance of all that he knew, and exhibit-
ing it in a clear and forcible manner ; so that knowledge,
which we often see to be no better than lumber in men of dull
understanding, was in him true, evident, and actual wisdom[2].'
His voice was strong, his utterance slow and deliberate, and
his words as accurate as they were vigorous. He delighted in
club-life. ' A tavern-chair,' he said, ' was the throne of human
felicity[3].' Of the clubs to which he belonged one is likely to
be immortal in fame. There he met in most friendly intercourse
Joshua Reynolds, the greatest painter that England had
seen, Edmund Burke, her greatest orator, David Garrick, her
greatest actor, James Boswell, her greatest biographer, and
Oliver Goldsmith, ' *qui nullum fere scribendi genus non
tetigit, nullum quod tetigit non ornavit*[4].' There were other
famous men besides who ' relished the manly conversation and
the society of the brown table[5] ' of the Literary Club—Edward
Gibbon, of the *Decline and Fall*, and Adam Smith, of the
Wealth of Nations, Charles James Fox, the orator and states-
man, R. B. Sheridan, who was as yet famous only for his
comedies, Bishop Percy, who saved for us the reliques that
were left of the old ballads, and Sir William Jones, the great
Orientalist. Among other clubable men of less fame, but still of
great merit, were Johnson's two friends, Bennet Langton, and
Topham Beauclerk—Langton, one of the best Greek scholars
of his day, as he was one of the worthiest of men ; Beauclerk,
who inherited from his ancestors Charles II. and Nell
Gwynne not only wit, liveliness, and an admirable skill as
a teller of good stories, but unhappily looseness of morals.

From this brilliant society Johnson returned to a home
which he shared with Miss Williams, the orphan daughter
of a man of learning, on whose blindness and poverty he

---

[1] Boswell's *Life of Johnson*, ii. 118.   [2] *Ib.* iv. 427.
[3] *Ib.* ii. 452, *n.* 1.   [4] *Ib.* iii. 82.   [5] *Ib.* iii. 128, *n.* 4.

took compassion, and with Mr. Levett, 'an obscure practiser
in physic, of a strange grotesque appearance, stiff and
formal in his manner, who seldom said a word while any
company was present[1].' In their society he found, however,
pleasure, though Miss Williams, in the long illness which
ended in her death, tried, but never exhausted, his patience.
Levett's memory he has celebrated in lines which have
touched many a heart. Thackeray said that he never could
read them without tears. Johnson, towards the close of his
life, sheltered moreover in his house some poor ladies who
had only one recommendation—their distress. Goldsmith,
hearing Boswell wonder that Johnson was very kind to
a man of a very bad character, replied : ' He is now become
miserable, and that insures the protection of Johnson[2].'
His charity was no sudden impulse, and no sudden effort.
Day after day, and month after month, he patiently endured
the discord caused by these peevish inmates. Happily, for
some fifteen or sixteen years, he had a second and a far
more splendid home. Henry Thrale, a wealthy brewer, 'a
good scholar and a man of a sound understanding[3],' had
a great relish for his conversation. His wife, who is perhaps
better known by her second husband's name, Piozzi, a
woman of some reading, of great vivacity and quickness
of mind, admired the rough philosopher as much as did her
husband. They appropriated to him a room in their town
house and in their villa at Streatham. He visited them
whenever he liked, and stayed as long as he pleased. ' Her
kindness soothed,' to use Johnson's grateful words, ' twenty
years of a life radically wretched[4].' He amply repaid what
he received by the constancy and the strength of his friendship, by the charm of his talk, by the brilliant friends whom
he gathered about him at their table, and by the fame which
he has given them. Since his day brewers have been raised
to the peerage, but no patent of nobility conferred by

[1] Boswell's *Life of Johnson*, i. 243.   [2] *Ib*. i. 417.
[3] *Ib*. i. 494.   [4] *Ib*. i. 520.

a monarch is likely to outlast that which Johnson gave to this Southwark trader.

If the friendship of James Boswell did not add so much to his comfort as did that of the Thrales, it has added far more to his fame. No hero was ever equally happy in his biographer, and no biographer was ever equally happy in his hero. Like the two halves of some wide-spreading arch each supports the other. The flood of time which sweeps so much away has swept all round it, but it stands stronger than ever.

This was by far the happiest part of Johnson's life. He was able to gratify his curiosity and to indulge in the pleasure of travelling. 'Life,' he once said, as he was driven rapidly along in a post-chaise, 'has not many better things than this[1].' With Reynolds he visited the West of England, with the Thrales he spent some weeks in Wales and some in France, and with Boswell he made his famous tour to the Hebrides. A trip which he projected to Italy was stopped at the last moment by the sudden death of Mr. Thrale's son. When he had almost reached his seventieth year, he showed that 'there was nothing of the old man about him[2]' by writing what is only the second, if indeed it is the second, of his works. The *Dictionary* was the greater achievement, but, unlike it, the *Lives of the Poets* can never be superseded. 'The enthusiasm with which the *Dictionary* was hailed[3]' can scarcely be understood now, though still by the student 'a leisure hour may always be very agreeably spent in turning over its pages[4].' The delight which was enjoyed by the first readers of the *Lives* can happily still be felt by their descendants. In their own way they remain unequalled.

The gloom which had covered so much of Johnson's life had been greatly dispersed. His circumstances were easy, his health was better than it had been since his youth, his

---

[1] Boswell's *Life of Johnson*, ii. 453.   [2] *Ib*. iii. 336.
[3] Macaulay's *Misc. Writings*, ed. 1871, p. 382.   [4] *Ib*.

fame was great and was greatly enjoyed by him. He had in large measure—

> 'that which should accompany old age,
> As honour, love, obedience, troops of friends [1].'

But the clouds gathered once more. The death of the two inmates who had lived with him for nearly thirty years 'had made his house,' as he sadly said, 'a solitude [2].' The ranks of his friends began to thin rapidly, as one dropped off after the other; but the greatest gap was made by the loss of Thrale. 'I looked for the last time upon the face that for fifteen years had never been turned upon me but with respect and benignity [3].' So Johnson recorded a few days after he had 'felt the last flutter of his pulse.' For a time he still had his Streatham 'home'—so he delighted to call it; but as months passed on, it was seen that it was in the 'plain, independent' brewer, not in his sprightly wife, that the constancy of friendship had existed. She began to weary of her old friends. Forgetful of her three living children, and of the nine whom she had lost, she was carried away by a violent passion for an Italian music-master; a man, indeed, of an irreproachable character. 'That house is lost to me for ever,' Johnson tremulously exclaimed, as he one day drove from Streatham with Miss Burney [4]. He made 'a parting use of the library,' reading in it St. Paul's touching farewell [5], and uttering a prayer for the family in the midst of which he had spent so many happy hours. He attended the church for the last time. '*Templo valedixi cum osculo,*' he recorded [6]. It was in Streatham that the hours of sickness and suffering that were now coming upon him should have been soothed by a woman's hand. She to whom he had been almost as a father, 'who had loved her with virtuous affection, who had honoured her with sincere esteem, who for a great part of human life had done her

---

[1] *Macbeth*, Act v. Sc. 3. [2] Boswell's *Life of Johnson*, iv. 241.
[3] *Ib.* iv. 84. [4] *Ib.* iv. 158, *n.* 4. [5] *Acts* xx. 17 to end.
[6] Boswell's *Life of Johnson*, iv. 159.

what good he could, and had never done her evil [1],' left him,
distressed and broken down by a complication of sufferings,
'to gasp his last in the river fog and coal smoke of Fleet-
street [2].' With her musical husband she had hastened to
enjoy the bright skies of sunny Italy. Johnson was laid to
rest in that spot where he had hoped to find a grave.

> 'Forsitan et nostrum nomen miscebitur istis [3],'

he had once said to Goldsmith, as they surveyed the Poets
Corner [4]. There, among the famous dead, we can read the
fine Latin epitaph with which the elder of the two men
graced the walls of Westminster Abbey and the memory of
his friend ; and there, as we cast down our eyes we trace
on the massy stone beneath our feet the name of Samuel
Johnson.

THE HISTORY OF RASSELAS, PRINCE OF ABYSSINIA.

'The miseries of life would be increased beyond all human
power of endurance, if we were to enter the world with the
same opinions as we carry from it.' So Johnson wrote in one
of the last of his *Ramblers* [5], when the sands of life were
rapidly running out in the glass that Death held before his
wife. A few weeks passed by, and in the sight of God he was
recording his purposes as she lay dead before him [6]. He
felt, to use his own words, how by the death of a wife 'the
continuity of being is lacerated ; the settled course of sentiment and action is stopped ; and life stands suspended and
motionless till it is driven by external causes into a new
channel [7].' Three years passed on, and his great *Dictionary*
was ready for publication, that noble piece of work which
had been done 'not in the soft obscurities of retirement, or

---

[1] Boswell's *Life of Johnson*, iv. 229, *n.* 3.

[2] Macaulay's *Misc. Writings*, ed. 1871, p. 413.

[3] Ovid. *Ars. Am.* iii. 339.   [4] Boswell's *Life of Johnson*, ii. 238.

[5] No. 196.   [6] Boswell's *Life of Johnson*, i. 354, *n.* 2.

[7] *Ib*. iii. 419.

under the shelter of academic bowers, but amidst incon-
venience and distraction, in sickness and in sorrow. I have
protracted my work,' he continued, 'till most of those whom
I wished to please have sunk into the grave ; and success
and miscarriage are empty sounds[1].' Four more years went
by, years of gloom and poverty. 'His mind, strained and
overlaboured by constant exertion, called for an interval
of repose and indolence. But indolence was the time of
danger; it was then that his spirits, not employed abroad,
turned with inward hostility against himself[2].' Repose,
however, whether it was a curse or a blessing, was not at
this time for him. 'He found that the great fame of his
Dictionary had not set him above the necessity of "making
provision for the day that was passing over him[3]." He was
arrested for debt. The man who was 'the chief glory' of his
age[4], whose life had been laborious and frugal, could not pay
five pounds eighteen shillings. It was by the benevolence
of Richardson the novelist that he was saved from that
'picture of hell upon earth,' a debtors' prison[5]. His lodgings
were mean, and, if we may trust his friend Miss Reynolds,
at this time 'he literally dressed like a beggar[6].' When
Reynolds brought Roubiliac the sculptor to visit him, 'he
took them up into a garret, which he considered as his
library : where, besides his books, all covered with dust,
there was an old crazy deal table, and a still worse and older
elbow chair having only three legs. In this chair Johnson
seated himself, after having, with considerable dexterity and
evident practice, first drawn it up against the wall, which
served to support it on that side on which the leg was defi-
cient[7].' The gloom had not as yet surrounded him on all sides.

---

[1] Boswell's *Life of Johnson*, i. 297.   [2] *Ib.* i. 268, *n.* 4.   [3] *Ib.* i. 303.

[4] 'The chief glory of every people,' he wrote, 'arises from its
authors,' *Ib.* i. 297, *n.* 3.

[5] So John Wesley three years earlier had described the Marshalsea
prison. *Ib.* i. 303, *n.* 1.

[6] *Ib.* i. 328, *n.* 1.   [7] *Ib.*

'Every heart must lean to somebody[1],' he said, and his still leant to his aged mother, far off though she was in Lichfield. He had one day been 'frighted with a black wafer' on a letter from that town. 'I was afraid,' he wrote, 'it had brought me ill news of my mother, whose death is one of the few calamities on which I think with terror[2].' She lived nine years longer, to comfort him, not with her presence, for they never met, but with the thought that she was still spared to him, with the hope that they might some day meet, and with her letters. 'He burned many letters in the last week of his life, and those written by his mother drew from him a flood of tears. One of his friends saw him cast a melancholy look upon their ashes, which he took up and examined to see if a word was still legible[3].'

It was on January 23, 1759, that the news came to him that 'the life which made his own life pleasant was at an end, and the gates of death were shut upon his prospects[4].' The first tidings of her illness 'pierced his heart[5].' 'Pray send me your blessing,' he wrote, 'and forgive all that I have done amiss to you. And whatever you would have done, and what debts you would have paid first, or anything else that you would direct, let Miss [Porter] put it down ; I shall endeavour to obey you. I have got twelve guineas to send you, but unhappily am at a loss how to send it to-night.' Six of these twelve guineas Johnson appears to have borrowed[6]. Had he had money he would at once have hastened to her dying bed. On January 20th he wrote to his step-daughter, 'I will, if it be possible, come down to you. God grant I may yet [find] my dear mother breathing and sensible. Do not tell her, lest I disappoint her. If I miss to write next post I am on the road[7].' On the other side he wrote to his mother, a letter which she was never to read. Her spirit had perhaps fled before he began to write.

---

[1] Boswell's *Life of Johnson*, i. 515.   [2] *Ib.* i. 212, *n.* 1.

[3] *Ib.* iv. 405, *n.* 1.   [4] *Ib.* i. 339, *n.* 3.   [5] *Ib.* i. 512.

[6] *Ib. n.* 1.   [7] *Ib.* i. 514.

'DEAR HONOURED MOTHER,

Neither your condition nor your character make it fit for me to say much. You have been the best mother, and I believe the best woman in the world. I thank you for your indulgence to me, and beg forgiveness of all that I have done ill, and all that I have omitted to do well. God grant you his Holy Spirit, and receive you to everlasting happiness, for Jesus Christ's sake. Amen. Lord Jesus receive your spirit. Amen.

I am, dear, dear mother,

Your dutiful son,

SAM. JOHNSON.'

Three days later he heard of her death. With the tenderness of conscience which always marked him he wrote:—'You will conceive my sorrow for the loss of my mother, of the best mother. If she were to live again surely I should behave better to her. But she is happy, and what is past is nothing to her; and for me, since I cannot repair my faults to her, I hope repentance will efface them.' He continues:—'I shall send a bill of twenty pounds in a few days, which I thought to have brought to my mother; but God suffered it not. I have not power or composure to say much more.' These twenty pounds he had earned by his *Rasselas*. While she was still breathing, while 'her weakness afflicted him beyond what he was willing to communicate to her,' he had to wrestle with poverty, and to call on his swelling heart for a book for which the booksellers would be willing to give him money. He would fain sit down and weep. But there was required of him a song and melody in his heaviness. It is little wonderful that the song was a song of sadness.

He had not only to write a story, but what to a man of his nature was no doubt still more painful, to make a bargain about it. He must have some money and have it quickly. On the very day on which he sent his last letter to his mother, he wrote to Mr. Strahan, the printer, as follows:—

'Sir,

When I was with you last night I told you of a story which I was preparing for the press. The title will be

"The Choice of Life

or

The History of . . . . . Prince of Abissinia."

It will make about two volumes like little Pompadour[1], that is about one middling volume. The bargain which I made with Mr. Johnson[2] was seventy five pounds (or guineas) a volume, and twenty-five pounds for the second edition. I will sell this either at that price or for sixty[3], the first edition of which he shall himself fix the number, and the property then to revert to me, or for forty pounds, and share the profit, that is retain half the copy. I shall have occasion for thirty pounds on Monday night, when I shall deliver the book which I must entreat you upon such delivery to procure me. I would have it offered to Mr. Johnson, but have no doubt of selling it, on some of the terms mentioned.

I will not print my name[4], but expect it to be known.

I am, dear Sir, your most humble servant,

SAM. JOHNSON.

Jan. 20, 1759.

Get me the money if you can[5].'

January 20th this year was a Saturday. Johnson had been writing the book all the week[6]. 'He told Sir Joshua Reynolds that he composed *Rasselas* in the evenings of one week, sent it to the press in portions as it was written, and had never since read it over.' It was on Saturday, January 13, that he seems first to have heard of his mother's danger; at all

---

[1] By 'little Pompadour,' Johnson, no doubt, means the second and cheaper edition of *The History of the Marchioness de Pompadour*, which had been just published.

[2] Mr. Johnson the bookseller was, I conjecture, W. Johnston, who, with Strahan and Dodsley, purchased the book.

[3] 'Fifty-five pounds' written first and then scored over.

[4] Johnson did not generally print his name to his books.

[5] Boswell's *Life of Johnson*, vi. xxviii.

[6] *Ib.* i. 341.

events his first letter *to* her bears that date. He must have
begun his story on the following Monday, and written it in hot
haste. If he worked seven days to the week he wrote each
evening more than seventeen pages of the present edition;
and if he rested on the Sunday he wrote more than twenty
pages. It would be a great effort for most people merely to
copy so much matter. That he sent it to the press in portions, as it was written, does not seem consistent with this
letter, and Sir Joshua's memory probably failed him on this
point. For the first edition Johnson received one hundred
pounds, and for the second twenty-five. His friend, the
Italian scholar, Baretti, says that 'any other person with the
degree of reputation he then possessed would have got £400
for that work, but Johnson never understood the art of
making the most of his productions[1].' With the money
that he received he defrayed the expenses of his mother's
funeral, and paid some little debts which she had left. The
house in which in her widowhood she had carried on her
husband's trade as a bookseller, though it was Johnson's
own, and though he was sorely tried by want of money, he
would not let or sell. He left it to his mother's old servant,
Catherine Chambers, for her use during her life-time. ' My
mother's debts,' he wrote, 'dear mother, I suppose I may
pay with little difficulty ; and the little trade may go silently
forward. I fancy Kitty can do nothing better ; and I shall
not want to put her out of a house, where she has lived so
long, and with so much virtue[2].'

The week of sorrow and strain and toil was at an end.
Did the memory of it, more than seventy years later, move
Thomas Carlyle to write the beautiful *Reminiscences* of his
father in the few days in which the old man lay dead in the
bed-chamber waiting for his burial ? If it did, it was a
memory rich in fruits.

The gloom which surrounded Johnson as in his garret in
Gough Square he wrote his story on The Choice of Life shows

---

[1] Boswell's *Life of Johnson*, i. 341, *n*. 3.   [2] *Ib*. i. 515.

itself in almost every page. Even in his happiest hours he would have written sadly of life. Great though the enjoyments were that he often found in it, yet when he thought of it he was never happy. Did the question rise ' whether life was upon the whole more happy or miserable, he was decidedly for the balance of misery [1].' With Imlac he would have always said:—' Human life is everywhere a state in which much is to be endured and little to be enjoyed [2].' But now, in the words of the old man whom Rasselas met in his moonlight walk along the bank of the Nile, he could have added with a sigh:—' I have neither mother to be delighted with the reputation of her son, nor wife to partake the honours of her husband [3].' And yet, in all his unhappiness, his loneliness, his poverty, his ill-health, not a complaint escapes his mouth. He might have said with the noble Venetian merchant :—

> ' I hold the world but as the world, Gratiano ;
> A stage where every man must play a part,
> And mine a sad one [4].'

But his part he played from first to last without whining. There was not a touch of bitterness in his nature. From Swift's savage humour and from Voltaire's biting irony he was equally free. Life is unhappy, but it may be made less unhappy by wisdom, by moderation, and by the resolute discharge of duty. Innocent pleasures must be enjoyed whenever they offer, and ' the short gleams of gaiety which life allows us' must not be needlessly clouded [5]. But after all, ' there is but one solid basis of happiness ; and that is, the reasonable hope of a happy futurity [6].' As for the choice of life, that choice which harasses us on the threshold of life, and troubles us in our course with idle regrets, to few indeed is it really free. With the hermit we must say :—' To him that lives well every form of life is good ; nor can I give any other

---

[1] Boswell's *Life of Johnson*, iv. 300.   [2] *Post*, p. 67.
[3] *Post*, p. 143.   [4] *Merchant of Venice*, i. 1. 77.
[5] *Post*, p. 119.   [6] Boswell's *Life of Johnson*, iii. 363.

rule for choice than to remove from all apparent evil[1].' The
poet Imlac tells the same lesson. ' Very few,' he said, 'live
by choice ; every man is placed in his present condition by
causes which acted without his foresight, and with which he
did not always willingly co-operate[2].' This is a truth—if,
that is to say, it be a truth—which Johnson often enforced.
In *The Idler*[3] he puts it in the mouth of ' Omar the prudent,' a man who had passed seventy-five years in making
schemes of life, none of which came to anything. ' " Young
man," said Omar, " it is of little use to form plans of life." '
To Boswell, Johnson writes :—' To prefer one future mode of
life to another upon just reasons requires faculties which it
has not pleased our Creator to give us[4].' In his diary he
records :—' Scarcely any man persists in a course of life
planned by choice, but as he is restrained from deviation by
some external power. He who may live as he will, seldom
lives long in the observation of his own rules[5].' To his hero
he shows the different states of life. ' Surely,' says the
young Prince, as hopeful as he was trustful, ' surely happiness
is somewhere to be found[6].' But youth he finds lost in folly,
acting without a plan, sad or cheerful only by chance, and
following a course of life which should cause shame, and was
certain if it came to old age to bring misery and remorse. The
teachers of morality he sees powerless to support their own
unhappiness by their 'polished periods and studied sentences[7],'
and the hermit has to own to him that a life such as his
will be certainly miserable, but not certainly devout[8]. The
philosopher who directs his hearers to live according to
nature he discovers to be ' one of the sages whom he should
understand less as he heard him longer[9]'; and the astronomer,
learned, benevolent, gifted with knowledge and many virtues,
is one more instance how ' of the uncertainties of our present

---

[1] *Post*, p. 88.   [2] *Post*, p. 80.   [3] No. 101.
[4] Boswell's *Life of Johnson*, ii. 22.   [5] *Ib.* ii. 114.
[6] *Post*, p. 80.   [7] *Post*, p. 84.   [8] *Post*, p. 89.   [9] *Post*, p. 92.

state the most dreadful and alarming is the uncertain continuance of reason [1].' Next the sage, cheerful though his
virtuous old age seemed to be, when questioned, said that 'to
him the world had lost its novelty'; that the praise which he
had justly earned 'was to an old man an empty sound,' and that
'it was enough that old age could obtain ease [2].' In the tents
of the shepherds, in the midst of that pastoral life whose innocence and happiness have been celebrated by the poets, there
was found rudeness and ignorance and stupid malevolence [3].
The prosperous man, liberal, wealthy, and hospitable, by his
very prosperity was in the greatest danger, and lived in
terror of the Bashaw [4]. The Bashaw, in all his power and
splendour was scarcely more secure than the man who
dreaded him. 'The letters of revocation arrived, he was
carried in chains to Constantinople, and his name was
mentioned no more [5].' The Sultan himself was 'subject to
the torments of suspicion, and the dread of enemies,' and
after advancing and deposing a second Bashaw, 'was murdered by the Janizaries [6].' That happiness which was not
found in courts had not taken up her abode in private houses.
Among the very poor it was useless to look for her [7], but
neither was she to be seen among those of middle fortune.
With them were narrow thoughts, low wishes, and merriment
that was often artificial [8]. In most families there was discord, parents and children were at variance, 'age looked with
anger on the temerity of youth, and youth with contempt on the
scrupulosity of age [9].' Married life was commonly unhappy.
'I know not,' said the princess, 'whether marriage be more
than one of the innumerable modes of human misery [10].' Still
more unhappy was the lot of the unmarried. 'Marriage has
many pains, but celibacy has no pleasures [11].' Virtue was no
security for happiness. 'All that it can afford is quietness

[1] *Post*, p. 139.   [2] *Post*, p. 143.   [3] *Post*, p. 85.   [4] *Post*, p. 87.
[5] *Post*, p. 94.   [6] *Ib.*   [7] *Post*, p. 96.   [8] *Post*, p. 95.
[9] *Post*, p. 97.   [10] *Post*, p. 102.   [11] *Post* p. 99.

of conscience and a steady prospect of a happier state,' for ' all natural and almost all political evils are incident alike to the bad and good[1].' Whatever choice of life any one had made, one thing was certain—it had been a wrong one. ' Such is the state of life that none are happy but by the anticipation of change : the change itself is nothing ; when we have made it, the next wish is to change again[2].' The only men who supported life without complaint were the monks of St. Anthony, and their life was one 'not of uniform delight, but uniform hardship[3].' Their safeguards against misery were three. They had to work for their livelihood, their time was regularly distributed, and their devotion made them ready for that other world which it kept always in their thoughts.

Such is the world that passes, almost as if upon some stage, before the eyes of Rasselas—the young prince whose noble nature could not be satisfied with the pleasures of a *Happy Valley*, but was full of longings for some higher, if some harder life. He is for the most part happier than the world that he gazes upon as some spectator, for he is full of eager plans, of ardent curiosity, and of 'visionary bustle.' Hope never leaves him to the last. His nature is trustful and innocent. He has wronged no one, and cannot readily believe in human wickedness. When Imlac tells him of pride and envy, 'he does not doubt of the facts which he relates, but imagines that he imputes them to mistaken motives[4].' He loves truth, and thinks it 'as treason against the great republic of human nature to make any man's virtues the means of deceiving him, whether on great or little occasions[5].' His nature is deeper than his sister's. She smiles at the story of the astronomer's madness, but he is deeply affected to see so noble a mind o'erthrown. His great longing is to govern some little kingdom justly[6] ; but never being forced to make a choice of life he passes away from our view still a dreamer and a mere spectator of men.

[1] *Post*, p. 101.   [2] *Post*, p. 150.   [3] *Post*, p. 151.
[4] *Post*, p. 59.   [5] *Post*, p. 145.   [6] *Post*, p. 158.

In Imlac, Johnson perhaps paints himself as he thinks that he might have been had the choice of life ever been his. He was a man who had lived in courts, was 'exercised in business, stored with observation [1].' He had 'found the delight of knowledge, and felt the pleasure of intelligence and the pride of invention,' and from that day 'began silently to despise riches [2].' He had wandered far and wide, 'drinking at the fountains of knowledge to quench the thirst of curiosity [3].' With Johnson he would have said: 'Curiosity is in great and generous minds the first passion and the last; and perhaps always predominates in proportion to the strength of the contemplative faculties [4].' He was a dreamer who was given 'to forming schemes for his conduct in different situations, in not one of which he was ever placed [5].' He was a humourist who could laugh at himself. He had longed to be a poet, and had soon found the important truth 'that no man was ever great by imitation [6].' He had studied man and nature and all the modes of life, but at last he saw that of a poet so much is required that he convinces Rasselas, if he does not convince himself, that to be a poet is in the power of no human being [7]. Twenty years of wandering had not however chilled his fires, and he still felt at times 'the enthusiastic fit [8].' He is free from all envy, malignity, or cynicism. He takes pleasure in the company of the young. He 'pities Rasselas's ignorance and loves his curiosity [9].' He never 'forces on him unwelcome knowledge, which time itself would too soon impress [10].' On the contrary he smiles as he remembers, 'that at the same age he was equally confident of unmingled prosperity, and equally fertile of consolatory expedients [11].' His heart had lost none of its tenderness. He was the only man to whom the astronomer 'could impart his troubles [12].' 'His trade was wisdom [13].' He

---

[1] Johnson's *Shakespeare*, ed. 1765, viii. 183 note.　　[2] *Post*, p. 56.
[3] *Post*, p. 57.　　[4] *The Rambler*, No. 150.　　[5] *Post*, p. 58.
[6] *Post*, p. 61.　　[7] *Post*, p. 64.　　[8] *Ib.*　　[9] *Post*, p. 54.
[10] *Post*, p. 144.　　[11] *Ib.*　　[12] *Post*, p. 150.
[13] Boswell's *Life of Johnson*, iii. 137, *n.* 1.

moralises on everything that he meets—on life in all its forms, on the nature of the soul, on death and immortality. He briefly tells the story of his life. ' "Sir," said Imlac, "my history will not be long : the life that is devoted to knowledge passes silently away, and is very little diversified by events. To talk in public, to think in solitude, to read and to hear, to inquire and answer inquiries, is the business of a scholar. He wanders about the world without pomp or terror, and is neither known nor valued but by men like himself[1]." ' What better or wiser guide could be found in the choice of life ? What then is the result of all his teaching ? As for the last time his little group of hearers stands round him 'in the mansions of the dead,' and hears him discourse on the nature of the soul, the Prince thus sums up the lesson that he has learnt : 'Those that lie here stretched before us, the wise and the powerful of ancient times, warn us to remember the shortness of our present state : they were perhaps snatched away while they were busy like us in the choice of life.' 'To me,' said the Princess, 'the choice of life is become less important; I hope hereafter to think only on the choice of eternity[2].' To both one and the other might have been answered the words which their guide had addressed to them earlier in the story. ' "It seems to me," said Imlac, "that while you are making the choice of life, you neglect to live[3]." '

The character of the Princess is wanting in dramatic power. She is sometimes Rasselas, sometimes Imlac, some-times undisguised Johnson. What she says is often very well said, but it might just as well, and often even better, have been said by a man. The lesser characters are more skilfully drawn, and sometimes by light touches of humour relieve the sadness of the story. Perhaps the best of all is the philosopher who discourses on the happiness of a life led according to nature, and who 'departed with the air of a man that had co-operated with the present system[4].'

[1] *Post*, p. 54. [2] *Post*, p. 157. [3] *Post*, p. 108. [4] *Post*, p. 92.

Is the picture that Johnson here draws of life in the main true, or is it surcharged with gloom? Each man can answer this question for himself, but may find it hard to speak for others. The young may well exclaim in the words of one poet :—

> 'Your wisdom may be more than ours,
>   But you have spent your golden hours[1].'

(not that Johnson ever had many golden hours to spend), or in the words of another poet :—

> 'How good is man's life, the mere living! how fit to employ
>   All the heart and the soul and the senses for ever in joy![2]'

They may call to mind Johnson's words that 'the miseries of life would be increased beyond all human power of endurance, if we were to enter the world with the same opinions as we carry from it[3].' They may refuse to trouble themselves with thoughts which would send them with downcast hearts and not half their strength into that battle of life which none can hope to escape. The answer that older men will give will depend on their temperament and on the way in which the world has treated them. Far too many, as they come to the last page, and read 'the conclusion in which nothing is concluded,' will own with a sigh how true is this sad picture of the life of man. Happily there will be found not a few who, as they look back on the long path that they have traversed, will bear a steady testimony that this world, with all its troubles, has a far brighter face than it turned on poor Johnson.

The young man on the threshold of life, ardent and hopeful, 'towering in the confidence[4]' of youth, may well be troubled in mind when he is told by one who had more of 'homely wisdom[5]' than any man of his age, that 'very few live by choice[6].' Let him remember that the last thing that Johnson meant to teach was the fatal indolence of

---

[1] Landor's *Works*, ed. 1876, v. 407.   [2] Browning's *Saul.*
[3] *Ante*, p. 20.   [4] Boswell's *Life of Johnson*, i. 324.
[5] Macaulay's *Essays*, ed. 1843, i. 400.   [6] *Post*, p. 80.

indecision.　Because we cannot choose we are not therefore
to do nothing. 'While we are making the choice of life,'
we are not 'to neglect to live[1].'　Let 'the young enthusiast[2],'
as he closes *Rasselas*, chase away any sadness or de-
spondency that may have come over him, by listening once
more to that 'road-melody or marching music of mankind,'
which Thomas Carlyle, translating from the greatest of
German poets, addressed to the students of Edinburgh :—

> 'The Future hides in it
> Gladness and sorrow;
> We press still thorow,
> Nought that abides in it
> Daunting us,—onward.
>
> And solemn before us,
> Veiled, the dark Portal;
> Goal of all mortal :—
> Stars silent rest o'er us,
> Graves under us silent!
>
> While earnest thou gazest,
> Comes boding of terror,
> Comes phantasm and error;
> Perplexes the bravest
> With doubt and misgiving.
>
> But heard are the Voices,
> Heard are the Sages,
> The Worlds and the Ages :
> Choose well; your choice is
> Brief, and yet endless.
>
> Here eyes do regard you
> In Eternity's stillness;
> Here is all fulness,
> Ye brave, to reward you;
> Work, and despair not[3].'

---

[1] *Post*, p. 108.
[2] *The Vanity of Human Wishes*, l. 136.
[3] Thomas Carlyle, *Inaugural Address at Edinburgh.*

CHIEF EVENTS IN THE LIFE OF

SAMUEL JOHNSON,

1709. Birth.
1728. Enters Pembroke College, Oxford.
1735. Publishes *Lobo's Abyssinia*. Marriage.
1737. Removes to London.
1738. *London.*
1740-3. *Debates.*
1744. *Life of Savage.*
1745. *Miscellaneous Observations on Macbeth.*
1747. *Plan for a Dictionary of the English Language.*
1749. *Vanity of Human Wishes. Irene* acted.
1750-2. *The Rambler.*
1752. Death of his wife.
1753. *The Adventurer.*
1755. Publication of *The Dictionary.*
1756. *Proposals for an edition of Shakespeare.*
1758-60. *The Idler.*
1759. Death of his mother. *Rasselas.*
1762. Pensioned.
1763. Gets to know Boswell.
1764. Literary Club founded.
    (or 1765) Gets to know the Thrales.
1765. *Edition of Shakespeare.*
1773. Tour to Scotland.
1775. *Journey to the Western Islands.*
1779. First four volumes of *The Lives of the Poets.*
1781. Last six volumes of *The Lives of the Poets*. Death of Thrale.
1784. Mrs. Thrale's second marriage. Death.

THE

HISTORY OF RASSELAS

PRINCE OF ABYSSINIA

THE

HISTORY OF RASSELAS,

PRINCE OF ABYSSINIA.

CHAPTER I.

DESCRIPTION OF A PALACE IN A VALLEY.

YE who listen with credulity to the whispers of fancy, and pursue with eagerness the phantoms of hope, who expect that age will perform the promises of youth, and that the deficiencies of the present day will be supplied by the morrow,—attend to the history of Rasselas, prince of Abyssinia.

Rasselas was the fourth son of the mighty emperor, in whose dominions the Father of Waters begins his course; whose bounty pours down the streams of plenty, and scatters over half the world the harvests of Egypt.

According to the custom which has descended from age to age among the monarchs of the torrid zone, Rasselas was confined in a private palace, with the other sons and daughters of Abyssinian royalty, till the order of succession should call him to the throne.

The place which the wisdom or policy of antiquity had destined for the residence of the Abyssinian princes, was a spacious valley in the kingdom of Amhara, surrounded on

every side by mountains, of which the summits overhang
the middle part. The only passage by which it could be
entered, was a cavern that passed under a rock, of which
it has long been disputed whether it was the work of
nature or of human industry. The outlet of the cavern
was concealed by a thick wood, and the mouth which
opened into the valley was closed with gates of iron, forged
by the artificers of ancient days, so massy that no man could
without the help of engines open or shut them.

From the mountains on every side, rivulets descended,
that filled all the valley with verdure and fertility, and
formed a lake in the middle, inhabited by fish of every
species, and frequented by every fowl whom nature has
taught to dip the wing in water. This lake discharged its
superfluities by a stream, which entered a dark cleft of the
mountain on the northern side, and fell with dreadful noise
from precipice to precipice till it was heard no more.

The sides of the mountains were covered with trees; the
banks of the brooks were diversified with flowers; every
blast shook spices from the rocks, and every month dropped
fruits upon the ground. All animals that bite the grass, or
browse the shrub, whether wild or tame, wandered in this
extensive circuit, secured from beasts of prey by the mountains
which confined them. On one part were flocks and herds
feeding in the pastures, on another all the beasts of chase
frisking in the lawns; the sprightly kid was bounding on the
rocks, the subtle monkey frolicing in the trees, and the
solemn elephant reposing in the shade. All the diversities
of the world were brought together; the blessings of nature
were collected, and its evils extracted and excluded.

The valley, wide and fruitful, supplied its inhabitants with
the necessaries of life, and all delights and superfluities were
added at the annual visit which the emperor paid his children,
when the iron gate was opened to the sound of music, and,

during eight days, every one that resided in the valley was required to propose whatever might contribute to make seclusion pleasant, to fill up the vacancies of attention, and lessen the tediousness of time. Every desire was immediately granted. All the artificers of pleasure were called to gladden the festivity ; the musicians exerted the power of harmony, and the dancers showed their activity before the princes, in hope that they should pass their lives in this blissful captivity, to which those only were admitted whose performance was thought able to add novelty to luxury. Such was the appearance of security and delight which this retirement afforded, that they to whom it was new always desired that it might be perpetual; and as those on whom the iron gate had once closed were never suffered to return, the effect of longer experience could not be known. Thus every year produced new schemes of delight, and new competitors for imprisonment.

The palace stood on an eminence, raised about thirty paces above the surface of the lake. It was divided into many squares or courts, built with greater or less magnificence, according to the rank of those for whom they were designed. The roofs were turned into arches of massy stone, joined by a cement that grew harder by time ; and the building stood from century to century, deriding the solstitial rains and equinoctial hurricanes, without need of reparation.

This house, which was so large as to be fully known to none but some ancient officers who successively inherited the secrets of the place, was built as if suspicion herself had dictated the plan. To every room there was an open and secret passage ; every square had a communication with the rest, either from the upper stories by private galleries, or by subterranean passages from the lower apartments. Many of the columns had unsuspected cavities, in which a long race

of monarchs had deposited their treasures. They then closed
up the opening with marble, which was never to be removed
but in the utmost exigencies of the kingdom; and recorded
their accumulations in a book, which was itself concealed in
a tower, not entered but by the emperor, attended by the
prince who stood next in succession.

CHAPTER II

THE DISCONTENT OF RASSELAS IN THE HAPPY VALLEY.

HERE the sons and daughters of Abyssinia lived only to
know the soft vicissitudes of pleasure and repose, attended
by all that were skilful to delight, and gratified with whatever the senses can enjoy. They wandered in gardens of
fragrance, and slept in the fortresses of security. Every art
was practised to make them pleased with their own condition. The sages who instructed them, told them of nothing
but the miseries of public life, and described all beyond the
mountains as regions of calamity, where discord was always
raging, and where man preyed upon man.

To heighten their opinion of their own felicity, they were
daily entertained with songs, the subject of which was *the
happy valley*. Their appetites were excited by frequent
enumerations of different enjoyments; and revelry and merriment was the business of every hour, from the dawn of
morning to the close of even.

These methods were generally successful: few of the
princes had ever wished to enlarge their bounds, but passed
their lives in full conviction that they had all within their
reach that art or nature could bestow, and pitied those
whom fate had excluded from this seat of tranquillity, as the
sport of chance and the slaves of misery.

Thus they rose in the morning and lay down at night,

pleased with each other and with themselves,—all but Rasselas, who, in the twenty-sixth year of his age, began to withdraw himself from their pastimes and assemblies, and to delight in solitary walks and silent meditation. He often sat before tables covered with luxury, and forgot to taste the dainties that were placed before him; he rose abruptly in the midst of the song, and hastily retired beyond the sound of music. His attendants observed the change, and endeavoured to renew his love of pleasure; he neglected their officiousness, repulsed their invitations, and spent day after day on the banks of rivulets sheltered with trees, where he sometimes listened to the birds in the branches, sometimes observed the fish playing in the stream, and anon cast his eyes upon the pastures and mountains filled with animals, of which some were biting the herbage, and some sleeping among the bushes.

This singularity of his humour made him much observed. One of the sages, in whose conversation he had formerly delighted, followed him secretly, in hope of discovering the cause of his disquiet. Rasselas, who knew not that any one was near him, having for some time fixed his eyes upon the goats that were browsing among the rocks, began to compare their condition with his own.

'What,' said he, 'makes the difference between man and all the rest of the animal creation? Every beast that strays beside me has the same corporeal necessities with myself: he is hungry and crops the grass, he is thirsty and drinks the stream; his thirst and hunger are appeased, he is satisfied and sleeps; he arises again and is hungry; he is again fed and is at rest. I am hungry and thirsty like him, but when thirst and hunger cease I am not at rest; I am like him pained with want, but am not like him satisfied with fulness. The intermediate hours are tedious and gloomy; I long again to be hungry, that I may again quicken my attention.

The birds peck the berries or the corn, and fly away to the groves, where they sit in seeming happiness on the branches, and waste their lives in tuning one unvaried series of sounds. I likewise can call the lutanist and the singer; but the sounds that pleased me yesterday weary me to-day, and will grow yet more wearisome to-morrow. I can discover within me no power of perception which is not glutted with its proper pleasure; yet I do not feel myself delighted. Man surely has some latent sense for which this place affords no gratification; or he has some desires distinct from sense, which must be satisfied before he can be happy.'

After this he lifted up his head, and seeing the moon rising, walked towards the palace. As he passed through the fields, and saw the animals around him, ' Ye,' said he, ' are happy, and need not envy me that walk thus among you, burdened with myself; nor do I, ye gentle beings, envy your felicity, for it is not the felicity of man. I have many distresses from which ye are free; I fear pain when I do not feel it; I sometimes shrink at evils recollected, and sometimes start at evils anticipated: surely the equity of Providence has balanced peculiar sufferings with peculiar enjoyments.'

With observations like these the prince amused himself as he returned, uttering them with a plaintive voice, yet with a look that discovered him to feel some complacence in his own perspicacity, and to receive some solace of the miseries of life, from consciousness of the delicacy with which he felt, and the eloquence with which he bewailed them. He mingled cheerfully in the diversions of the evening, and all rejoiced to find that his heart was lightened.

CHAPTER III.

THE WANTS OF HIM THAT WANTS NOTHING.

On the next day, his old instructor, imagining that he had now made himself acquainted with his disease of mind, was in hope of curing it by counsel, and officiously sought an opportunity of conference, which the prince, having long considered him as one whose intellects were exhausted, was not very willing to afford: 'Why,' said he, 'does this man thus intrude upon me; shall I be never suffered to forget those lectures which pleased only while they were new, and to become new again must be forgotten?' He then walked into the wood, and composed himself to his usual meditations; when, before his thoughts had taken any settled form, he perceived his pursuer at his side, and was at first prompted by his impatience to go hastily away; but, being unwilling to offend a man whom he had once reverenced and still loved, he invited him to sit down with him on the bank.

The old man, thus encouraged, began to lament the change which had been lately observed in the prince, and to inquire why he so often retired from the pleasures of the palace to loneliness and silence. 'I fly from pleasure,' said the prince, 'because pleasure has ceased to please; I am lonely, because I am miserable, and am unwilling to cloud with my presence the happiness of others.' 'You, sir,' said the sage, 'are the first who has complained of misery in the *happy valley*. I hope to convince you that your complaints have no real cause. You are here in full possession of all that the emperor of Abyssinia can bestow; here is neither labour to be endured nor danger to be dreaded, yet here is all that labour or danger can procure or purchase. Look round and tell me which of your wants is without supply: if you want nothing, how are you unhappy?'

'That I want nothing,' said the prince, 'or that I know not what I want, is the cause of my complaint; if I had any known want, I should have a certain wish; that wish would excite endeavour, and I should not then repine to see the sun move so slowly towards the western mountain, or lament when the day breaks and sleep will no longer hide me from myself. When I see the kids and the lambs chasing one another, I fancy that I should be happy if I had something to pursue. But possessing all that I can want, I find one day and one hour exactly like another, except that the latter is still more tedious than the former. Let your experience inform me how the day may now seem as short as in my childhood, while nature was yet fresh, and every moment showed me what I never had observed before. I have already enjoyed too much; give me something to desire.'

The old man was surprised at this new species of affliction, and knew not what to reply, yet was unwilling to be silent. 'Sir,' said he, 'if you had seen the miseries of the world, you would know how to value your present state.' 'Now,' said the prince, 'you have given me something to desire; I shall long to see the miseries of the world, since the sight of them is necessary to happiness.'

CHAPTER IV.

THE PRINCE CONTINUES TO GRIEVE AND MUSE.

At this time the sound of music proclaimed the hour of repast, and the conversation was concluded. The old man went away sufficiently discontented, to find that his reasonings had produced the only conclusion which they were intended to prevent. But in the decline of life shame and grief are of short duration: whether it be that we bear easily what we have borne long; or that, finding ourselves in age less regarded, we less regard others; or, that we look with slight regard upon afflictions to which we know that the hand of death is about to put an end.

The prince, whose views were extended to a wider space, could not speedily quiet his emotions. He had been before terrified at the length of life which nature promised him, because he considered that in a long time much must be endured; he now rejoiced in his youth, because in many years much might be done.

This first beam of hope that had been ever darted into his mind, rekindled youth in his cheeks, and doubled the lustre of his eyes. He was fired with the desire of doing something, though he knew not yet with distinctness either end or means.

He was now no longer gloomy and unsocial; but, considering himself as master of a secret stock of happiness, which he could enjoy only by concealing it, he affected to be busy in all schemes of diversion, and endeavoured to make others pleased with the state of which he himself was weary. But pleasures never can be so multiplied or continued, as not to leave much of life unemployed; there were many hours, both of the night and day, which he could spend without suspicion in solitary thought. The load of life was much lightened: he went eagerly into the assemblies, because he supposed the frequency of his presence necessary to the success of his purposes; he retired gladly to privacy, because he had now a subject of thought.

His chief amusement was to picture to himself that world which he had never seen; to place himself in various conditions, to be entangled in imaginary difficulties, and to be engaged in wild adventures; but his benevolence always terminated his projects in the relief of distress, the detection of fraud, the defeat of oppression, and the diffusion of happiness.

Thus passed twenty months of the life of Rasselas. He busied himself so intensely in visionary bustle, that he forgot his real solitude, and, amidst hourly preparations for the various incidents of human affairs, neglected to consider by what means he should mingle with mankind.

One day, as he was sitting on a bank, he feigned to himself an orphan virgin robbed of her little portion by a treacherous lover, and crying after him for restitution and redress. So strongly was the image impressed upon his mind, that he started up in the maid's defence, and ran forward to seize the plunderer, with all the eagerness of real pursuit. Fear naturally quickens the flight of guilt. Rasselas could not catch the fugitive with his utmost efforts; but resolving to weary by perseverance, him whom he could not surpass in speed, he pressed on till the foot of the mountain stopped his course.

Here he recollected himself, and smiled at his own useless impetuosity. Then raising his eyes to the mountain, 'This,' said he, 'is the fatal obstacle that hinders at once the enjoyment of pleasure, and the exercise of virtue. How long is it that my hopes and wishes have flown beyond this boundary of my life, which yet I never have attempted to surmount!'

Struck with this reflection, he sat down to muse; and remembered, that since he first resolved to escape from his confinement, the sun had passed twice over him in his annual course. He now felt a degree of regret with which he had never been before acquainted. He considered how much might have been done, in the time which had passed and left nothing real behind it. He compared twenty months with the life of man. 'In life,' said he, 'is not to be counted the ignorance of infancy, or imbecility of age. We are long before we are able to think, and we soon cease from the power of acting. The true period of human existence may be reasonably estimated at forty years, of which I have mused away the four and twentieth part. What I have lost was certain, for I have certainly possessed it; but of twenty months to come who can assure me?'

The consciousness of his own folly pierced him deeply, and he was long before he could be reconciled to himself. 'The rest of my time,' said he, 'has been lost by the crime or folly of my ancestors, and the absurd institutions of my country; I remember it with disgust, yet without remorse: but the months that have passed since new light darted into my soul, since I formed a scheme of reasonable felicity, have been squandered by my own fault. I have lost that which can never be restored; I have seen the sun rise and set for twenty months, an idle gazer on the light of heaven: in this time the birds have left the nest of their mother, and committed themselves to the woods and to the skies; the kid has forsaken the teat, and learned by degrees to climb the rocks in quest of independent sustenance. I only have made no advances, but am still helpless and ignorant. The moon, by more than twenty changes, admonished me of the flux of life; the stream that rolled before my feet upbraided my inactivity. I sat feasting on intellectual luxury, regardless alike of the examples of the earth, and the instructions of the planets. Twenty months are passed; who shall restore them?'

These sorrowful meditations fastened upon his mind; he passed four months in resolving to lose no more time in idle resolves, and was awakened to more vigorous exertion, by hearing a maid, who had broken a porcelain cup, remark, that what cannot be repaired is not to be regretted.

This was obvious; and Rasselas reproached himself that he had not discovered it; having not known, or not considered, how many useful hints are obtained by chance, and how often the mind, hurried by her own ardour to distant views, neglects the truths that lie open before her. He for a few hours regretted his regret, and from that time bent his whole mind upon the means of escaping from the valley of happiness.

CHAPTER V.

THE PRINCE MEDITATES HIS ESCAPE.

He now found that it would be very difficult to effect that which it was very easy to suppose effected. When he looked round about him, he saw himself confined by the bars of nature, which had never yet been broken, and by the gate, through which none that once had passed it were ever able to return. He was now impatient as an eagle in a grate. He passed week after week in clambering the mountains, to see if there was any aperture which the bushes might conceal, but found all the summits inaccessible by their prominence. The iron gate he despaired to open; for it was not only secured with all the power of art, but was always watched by successive sentinels, and was by its position exposed to the perpetual observation of all the inhabitants.

He then examined the cavern through which the waters of the lake were discharged; and, looking down at a time when the sun shone strongly upon its mouth, he discovered it to be full of broken rocks, which, though they permitted the stream to flow through many narrow passages, would stop any body of solid bulk. He returned discouraged and dejected; but having now known the blessing of hope, resolved never to despair.

In these fruitless researches he spent ten months. The time, however, passed cheerfully away: in the morning he rose with new hope, in the evening applauded his own diligence, and in the night slept sound after his fatigue. He met a thousand amusements which beguiled his labour, and diversified his thoughts. He discerned the various instincts of animals and properties of plants, and found the place replete with wonders, of which he purposed to solace himself with the contemplation, if he should never be able to accomplish his flight; rejoicing that his endeavours, though yet unsuccessful, had supplied him with a source of inexhaustible inquiry.

But his original curiosity was not yet abated; he resolved to obtain some knowledge of the ways of men. His wish still continued, but his hope grew less. He ceased to survey any longer the walls of his prison, and spared to search by new toils for interstices which he knew could not be found, yet determined to keep his design always in view, and lay hold on any expedient that time should offer.

CHAPTER VI.

A DISSERTATION ON THE ART OF FLYING.

AMONG the artists that had been allured into the happy valley, to labour for the accommodation and pleasure of its inhabitants, was a man eminent for his knowledge of the mechanic powers, who had contrived many engines both of use and recreation. By a wheel which the stream turned, he forced the water into a tower, whence it was distributed to all the apartments of the palace. He erected a pavilion in the garden, around which he kept the air always cool by artificial showers. One of the groves, appropriated to the ladies, was ventilated by fans, to which the rivulets that ran through it gave a constant motion; and instruments of soft music were placed at proper distances, of which some played by the impulse of the wind, and some by the power of the stream.

This artist was sometimes visited by Rasselas, who was pleased with every kind of knowledge, imagining that the time would come when all his acquisitions should be of use to him in the open world. He came one day to amuse himself in his usual manner, and found the master busy in building a sailing chariot: he saw that the design was practicable upon a level surface, and with expressions of great esteem solicited its completion. The workman was pleased to find himself so much regarded by the prince, and resolved to gain yet higher honours. 'Sir,' said he, 'you have seen but a small part of what the mechanic sciences can perform. I have been long of opinion, that instead of the tardy conveyance of ships and chariots, man might use the swifter migration of wings; that the fields of air are open to knowledge, and that only ignorance and idleness need crawl upon the ground.'

This hint rekindled the prince's desire of passing the mountains: having seen what the mechanist had already performed, he was willing to fancy that he could do more; yet resolved to inquire further, before he suffered hope to afflict him by disappointment. 'I am afraid,' said he to the artist, 'that your imagination prevails over your skill, and that you now tell me rather what you wish, than what you know. Every animal has his element assigned him; the birds have the air, and man and beasts the earth.' 'So,' replied the mechanist, 'fishes have the water, in which yet beasts can swim by nature, and men by art. He that can swim needs not despair to fly; to swim is to fly in a grosser fluid, and to fly is to swim in a subtler. We are only to proportion our power of resistance to the different density of matter through which we are to pass. You will be necessarily upborne by the air, if you can renew any impulse upon it faster than the air can recede from the pressure.'

'But the exercise of swimming,' said the prince 'is very laborious; the strongest limbs are soon wearied: I am afraid the act of flying will be yet more violent; and wings will be of no great use, unless we can fly further than we can swim.'

'The labour of rising from the ground,' said the artist, 'will be great, as we see it in the heavier domestic fowls; but as we mount higher, the earth's attraction, and the body's gravity, will be gradually diminished, till we shall arrive at a region where the man will float in the air without any tendency to fall: no care will then be necessary but to move forwards, which the gentlest impulse will effect. You, sir, whose curiosity is so extensive, will easily conceive with what pleasure a philosopher, furnished with wings, and hovering in the sky, would see the earth, and all its inhabitants, rolling beneath him, and presenting to him successively, by its diurnal motion, all the countries within the same parallel. How must it amuse the pendent spectator to see the moving scene of land and ocean, cities, and deserts! To survey with equal security the marts of trade, and the fields of battle; mountains infested by barbarians, and fruitful regions gladdened by plenty and lulled by peace! How easily shall we then trace the Nile through all his passage; pass over to distant regions, and examine the face of nature from one extremity of the earth to the other!'

'All this,' said the prince, 'is much to be desired; but I am afraid that no man will be able to breathe in these regions of speculation and tranquillity. I have been toid that respiration is difficult upon lofty mountains; yet from these precipices, though so high as to produce great tenuity of air, it is very easy to fall; therefore I suspect, that from any height where life can be supported, there may be danger of too quick descent.'

'Nothing,' replied the artist, 'will ever be attempted, if all possible objections must be first overcome. If you will favour my project, I will try the first flight at my own hazard. I have considered the structure of all volant animals, and find the folding continuity of the bat's wings most easily accommodated to the human form. Upon this model I shall begin my task to-morrow, and in a year expect to tower into the air beyond the malice and pursuit of man. But I will work only on this condition, that the art shall not be divulged, and that you shall not require me to make wings for any but ourselves.'

'Why,' said Rasselas, 'should you envy others so great an advantage? All skill ought to be exerted for universal good; every man has owed much to others, and ought to repay the kindness that he has received.'

'If men were all virtuous,' returned the artist, 'I should with great alacrity teach them all to fly. But what would be the security of the good, if the bad could at pleasure invade them from the sky? Against an army sailing through the clouds, neither walls, nor mountains, nor seas, could afford any security. A flight of northern savages might hover in the wind, and light at once with irresistible violence upon the capital of a fruitful region that was rolling under them. Even this valley, the retreat of princes, the abode of happiness, might be violated by the sudden descent of some of the naked nations that swarm on the coast of the southern sea.'

The prince promised secresy, and waited for the performance, not wholly hopeless of success. He visited the work from time to time, observed its progress, and remarked many ingenious contrivances to facilitate motion, and unite levity with strength. The artist was every day more certain that he should leave vultures and eagles behind him, and the contagion of his confidence seized upon the prince.

In a year the wings were finished; and, on a morning appointed, the maker appeared furnished for flight on a little promontory : he waved his pinions awhile to gather air, then leaped from his stand, and in an instant dropped into the lake. His wings, which were of no use in the air, sustained him in the water, and the prince drew him to land, half dead with terror and vexation.

CHAPTER VII.

THE PRINCE FINDS A MAN OF LEARNING.

THE prince was not much afflicted by this disaster, having suffered himself to hope for a happier event, only because he had no other means of escape in view. He still persisted in his design to leave the happy valley by the first opportunity.

His imagination was now at a stand; he had no prospect of entering into the world ; and, notwithstanding all his endeavours to support himself, discontent by degrees preyed upon him, and he began again to lose his thoughts in sadness, when the rainy season, which in these countries is periodical, made it inconvenient to wander in the woods.

The rain continued longer and with more violence than had been ever known ; the clouds broke on the surrounding mountains, and the torrents streamed into the plain on every side, till the cavern was too narrow to discharge the water. The lake overflowed its banks, and all the level of the valley was covered with the inundation. The eminence on which the palace was built, and some other spots of rising ground, were all that the eye could now discover. The herds and flocks left the pastures, and both the wild beasts and the tame retreated to the mountains.

This inundation confined all the princes to domestic

amusements ; and the attention of Rasselas was particularly seized by a poem, which Imlac rehearsed, upon the various conditions of humanity. He commanded the poet to attend him in his apartment, and recite his verses a second time ; then entering into familiar talk, he thought himself happy in having found a man who knew the world so well, and could so skilfully paint the scenes of life. He asked a thousand questions about things, to which, though common to all other mortals, his confinement from childhood had kept
10 him a stranger. The poet pitied his ignorance, and loved his curiosity, and entertained him from day to day with novelty and instruction, so that the prince regretted the necessity of sleep, and longed till the morning should renew his pleasure.

As they were sitting together, the prince commanded Imlac to relate his history, and to tell by what accident he was forced, or by what motive induced, to close his life in the happy valley. As he was going to begin his narrative, Rasselas was called to a concert, and obliged to restrain his
20 curiosity till the evening.

CHAPTER VIII.

THE HISTORY OF IMLAC.

THE close of the day is, in the regions of the torrid zone, the only season of diversion and entertainment, and it was therefore midnight before the music ceased, and the princesses retired. Rasselas then called for his companion, and required him to begin the story of his life.

' Sir,' said Imlac, ' my history will not be long : the life that is devoted to knowledge passes silently away, and is
30 very little diversified by events. To talk in public, to think in solitude, to read and to hear, to inquire and answer in-

quiries, is the business of a scholar. He wanders about the world without pomp or terror, and is neither known nor valued but by men like himself.

'I was born in the kingdom of Goiama, at no great distance from the fountain of the Nile. My father was a wealthy merchant, who traded between the inland countries of Africk and the ports of the Red Sea. He was honest, frugal, and diligent, but of mean sentiments and narrow comprehension: he desired only to be rich, and to conceal his riches, lest he should be spoiled by the governors of the province.'

'Surely,' said the prince, 'my father must be negligent of his charge, if any man in his dominions dares take that which belongs to another. Does he not know that kings are accountable for injustice permitted as well as done? If I were emperor, not the meanest of my subjects should be oppressed with impunity. My blood boils when I am told that a merchant durst not enjoy his honest gains, for fear of losing them by the rapacity of power. Name the governor who robbed the people, that I may declare his crimes to the emperor.'

'Sir,' said Imlac, 'your ardour is the natural effect of virtue animated by youth: the time will come when you will acquit your father, and perhaps hear with less impatience of the governor. Oppression is, in the Abyssinian dominions, neither frequent nor tolerated; but no form of government has been yet discovered, by which cruelty can be wholly prevented. Subordination supposes power on one part, and subjection on the other; and if power be in the hands of men, it will sometimes be abused. The vigilance of the supreme magistrate may do much, but much will still remain undone. He can never know all the crimes that are committed, and can seldom punish all that he knows.'

'This,' said the prince, 'I do not understand; but I had rather hear thee than dispute. Continue thy narration.'

'My father,' proceeded Imlac, 'originally intended that I

should have no other education, than such as might qualify me for commerce; and discovering in me great strength of memory and quickness of apprehension, often declared his hope that I should be some time the richest man in Abyssinia.'

'Why,' said the prince, 'did thy father desire the increase of his wealth, when it was already greater than he durst discover or enjoy? I am unwilling to doubt thy veracity, yet inconsistencies cannot both be true.'

'Inconsistencies' answered Imlac, 'cannot both be right, but, imputed to man, they may both be true. Yet diversity is not inconsistency. My father might expect a time of greater security. However, some desire is necessary to keep life in motion; and he whose real wants are supplied, must admit those of fancy.'

'This,' said the prince, 'I can in some measure conceive. I repent that I interrupted thee.'

'With this hope,' proceeded Imlac, 'he sent me to school; but when I had once found the delight of knowledge, and felt the pleasure of intelligence and the pride of invention, I began silently to despise riches, and determined to disappoint the purpose of my father, whose grossness of conception raised my pity. I was twenty years old before his tenderness would expose me to the fatigue of travel, in which time I had been instructed, by successive masters, in all the literature of my native country. As every hour taught me something new, I lived in a continual course of gratification; but, as I advanced towards manhood, I lost much of the reverence with which I had been used to look on my instructors; because when the lesson was ended, I did not find them wiser or better than common men.

'At length my father resolved to initiate me in commerce, and opening one of his subterranean treasuries, counted out ten thousand pieces of gold. "This, young man," said he,

" is the stock with which you must negotiate. I began with less than the fifth part, and you see how diligence and parsimony have increased it. This is your own to waste or to improve. If you squander it by negligence or caprice, you must wait for my death before you will be rich; if in four years you double your stock, we will thenceforward let subordination cease, and live together as friends and partners; for he shall always be equal with me, who is equally skilled in the art of growing rich."

' We laid our money upon camels, concealed in bales of cheap goods, and travelled to the shore of the Red Sea. When I cast my eye on the expanse of waters, my heart bounded like that of a prisoner escaped. I felt an unextinguishable curiosity kindle in my mind, and resolved to snatch this opportunity of seeing the manners of other nations, and of learning sciences unknown in Abyssinia.

' I remembered that my father had obliged me to the improvement of my stock, not by a promise which I ought not to violate, but by a penalty which I was at liberty to incur ; and therefore determined to gratify my predominant desire, and, by drinking at the fountains of knowledge, to quench the thirst of curiosity.

' As I was supposed to trade without connexion with my father, it was easy for me to become acquainted with the master of a ship, and procure a passage to some other country. I had no motives of choice to regulate my voyage; it was sufficient for me that, wherever I wandered, I should see a country which I had not seen before. I therefore entered a ship bound for Surat, having left a letter for my father declaring my intention.

CHAPTER IX.

THE HISTORY OF IMLAC CONTINUED.

'When I first entered upon the world of waters, and lost
sight of land, I looked round about me with pleasing terror,
and thinking my soul enlarged by the boundless prospect,
imagined that I could gaze round for ever without satiety;
but in a short time I grew weary of looking on barren
uniformity, where I could only see again what I had already
seen. I then descended into the ship, and doubted for
10 awhile whether all my future pleasures would not end like
this, in disgust and disappointment. Yet, surely, said I, the
ocean and the land are very different; the only variety of
water is rest and motion, but the earth has mountains and
valleys, deserts and cities; it is inhabited by men of different
customs and contrary opinions; and I may hope to find
variety in life, though I should miss it in nature.

'With this thought I quieted my mind; and amused
myself during the voyage, sometimes by learning from the
sailors the art of navigation, which I have never practised,
20 and sometimes by forming schemes for my conduct in
different situations, in not one of which I have been ever
placed.

'I was almost weary of my naval amusements when we
landed safely at Surat. I secured my money, and pur-
chasing some commodities for show, joined myself to a
caravan that was passing into the inland country. My
companions, for some reason or other, conjecturing that I
was rich, and, by my inquiries and admiration, finding
that I was ignorant, considered me as a novice whom they
30 had a right to cheat, and who was to learn at the usual
expense the art of fraud. They exposed me to the theft

of servants and the exaction of officers, and saw me plun-
dered upon false pretences, without any advantage to themselves, but that of rejoicing in the superiority of their own
knowledge.'

'Stop a moment,' said the prince. 'Is there such de-
pravity in man, as that he should injure another without
benefit to himself? I can easily conceive that all are pleased
with superiority; but your ignorance was merely accidental,
which, being neither your crime nor your folly, could
afford them no reason to applaud themselves; and the 10
knowledge which they had, and which you wanted, they
might as effectually have shown by warning, as betraying
you.'

'Pride' said Imlac 'is seldom delicate, it will please
itself with very mean advantages; and envy feels not its own
happiness, but when it may be compared with the misery of
others. They were my enemies, because they grieved to
think me rich; and my oppressors, because they delighted
to find me weak.'

'Proceed,' said the prince: 'I doubt not of the facts which 20
you relate, but imagine that you impute them to mistaken
motives.'

'In this company,' said Imlac, 'I arrived at Agra, the
capital of Indostan, the city in which the great Mogul
commonly resides. I applied myself to the language of the
country, and in a few months was able to converse with the
learned men; some of whom I found morose and reserved,
and others easy and communicative; some were unwilling to
teach another what they had with difficulty learned themselves;
and some showed that the end of their studies was to gain 30
the dignity of instructing.

'To the tutor of the young princes I recommended
myself so much, that I was presented to the emperor as a
man of uncommon knowledge. The emperor asked me

many questions concerning my country and my travels;
and though I cannot now recollect any thing that he
uttered above the power of a common man, he dismissed
me astonished at his wisdom, and enamoured of his goodness.

'My credit was now so high, that the merchants with whom
I had travelled, applied to me for recommendations to the
ladies of the court. I was surprised at their confidence of
solicitation, and gently reproached them with their practices
on the road. They heard me with cold indifference, and
showed no tokens of shame or sorrow.

'They then urged their request with the offer of a bribe;
but what I would not do for kindness, I would not do for
money, and refused them, not because they had injured me,
but because I would not enable them to injure others; for I
knew they would have made use of my credit to cheat those
who should buy their wares.

'Having resided at Agra till there was no more to be
learned, I travelled into Persia, where I saw many remains
of ancient magnificence, and observed many new accommodations of life. The Persians are a nation eminently social,
and their assemblies afforded me daily opportunities of remarking characters and manners, and of tracing human
nature through all its variations.

'From Persia I passed into Arabia, where I saw a nation
at once pastoral and warlike; who live without any settled
habitation; whose only wealth is their flocks and herds;
and who have yet carried on through all ages an hereditary
war with all mankind, though they neither covet nor envy
their possessions.'

CHAPTER X.

IMLAC'S HISTORY CONTINUED. A DISSERTATION UPON POETRY.

'Wherever I went, I found that poetry was considered as the highest learning, and regarded with a veneration somewhat approaching to that which man would pay to the angelic nature. And yet it fills me with wonder, that, in almost all countries, the most ancient poets are considered as the best: whether it be that every other kind of knowledge is an acquisition gradually attained, and poetry is a gift conferred at once; or that the first poetry of every nation surprised them as a novelty, and retained the credit by consent, which it received by accident at first; or whether, as the province of poetry is to describe nature and passion, which are always the same, the first writers took possession of the most striking objects for description, and the most probable occurrences for fiction, and left nothing to those that followed them, but transcription of the same events, and new combinations of the same images :—whatever be the reason, it is commonly observed that the early writers are in possession of nature, and their followers of art; that the first excel in strength and invention, and the latter in elegance and refinement.

'I was desirous to add my name to this illustrious fraternity. I read all the poets of Persia and Arabia, and was able to repeat by memory the volumes that are suspended in the mosque of Mecca. But I soon found that no man was ever great by imitation. My desire of excellence impelled me to transfer my attention to nature and to life. Nature was to be my subject, and men to be my auditors: I could never describe what I had not seen; I could not hope to move those with delight or terror, whose interests and opinions I did not understand.

'Being now resolved to be a poet, I saw everything with a new purpose; my sphere of attention was suddenly magnified; no kind of knowledge was to be overlooked. I ranged mountains and deserts for images and resemblances, and pictured upon my mind every tree of the forest and flower of the valley. I observed with equal care the crags of the rock and the pinnacles of the palace. Sometimes I wandered along the mazes of the rivulet, and sometimes watched the changes of the summer clouds. To a poet nothing can be useless. Whatever is beautiful, and whatever is dreadful, must be familiar to his imagination: he must be conversant with all that is awfully vast or elegantly little. The plants of the garden, the animals of the wood, the minerals of the earth, and meteors of the sky, must all concur to store his mind with inexhaustible variety: for every idea is useful for the enforcement or decoration of moral or religious truth; and he who knows most, will have most power of diversifying his scenes, and of gratifying his reader with remote allusions and unexpected instruction.

'All the appearances of nature I was therefore careful to study; and every country which I have surveyed has contributed something to my poetical powers.'

'In so wide a survey,' said the prince, 'you must surely have left much unobserved. I have lived, till now, within the circuit of these mountains, and yet cannot walk abroad without the sight of something which I had never beheld before, or never heeded.'

'The business of a poet,' said Imlac, 'is to examine, not the individual, but the species; to remark general properties and large appearances. He does not number the streaks of the tulip, or describe the different shades in the verdure of the forest: he is to exhibit in his portraits of nature such prominent and striking features, as recal the original to every mind; and must neglect the minuter discriminations, which one may have remarked, and another have neglected, for those characteristics which are alike obvious to vigilance and carelessness.

'But the knowledge of nature is only half the task of a poet: he must be acquainted likewise with all the modes of life. His character requires that he estimate the happiness and misery of every condition, observe the power of all the passions in all their combinations, and trace the changes of the human mind as they are modified by various institutions and accidental influences of climate or custom, from the sprightliness of infancy to the despondence of decrepitude. He must divest himself of the prejudices of his age and country; he must consider right and wrong in their abstracted and invariable state; he must disregard present laws and opinions, and rise to general and transcendental truths, which will always be the same. He must therefore content himself with the slow progress of his name, contemn the applause of his own time, and commit his claims to the justice of posterity. He must write as the interpreter of nature, and the legislator of mankind, and consider himself as presiding over the thoughts and manners of future generations; as a being superior to time and place.

'His labour is not yet at an end; he must know many languages and many sciences; and, that his style may be worthy of his thoughts, must, by incessant practice, familiarise to himself every delicacy of speech and grace of harmony.'

CHAPTER XI.

IMLAC'S NARRATIVE CONTINUED.   A HINT ON PILGRIMAGE

IMLAC now felt the enthusiastic fit, and was proceeding to aggrandise his own profession, when the prince cried out, 'Enough! thou hast convinced me that no human being can ever be a poet.   Proceed with thy narration.'

'To be a poet,' said Imlac, 'is indeed very difficult.'

'So difficult,' returned the prince, 'that I will at present hear no more of his labours.   Tell me whither you went when you had seen Persia.'

'From Persia,' said the poet, 'I travelled through Syria, and for three years resided in Palestine, where I conversed with great numbers of the northern and western nations of Europe; the nations which are now in possession of all power and all knowledge; whose armies are irresistible, and whose fleets command the remotest parts of the globe. When I compared these men with the natives of our own kingdom, and those that surround us, they appeared almost another order of beings.   In their countries it is difficult to wish for anything that may not be obtained: a thousand arts, of which we never heard, are continually labouring for their convenience and pleasure; and whatever their own climate has denied them is supplied by their commerce.'

'By what means,' said the prince, 'are the Europeans thus powerful; or why, since they can so easily visit Asia and Africa for trade or conquest, cannot the Asiatics and Africans invade their coasts, plant colonies in their ports, and give laws to their natural princes?   The same wind that carries them back, would bring us thither.'

'They are more powerful, sir, than we,' answered Imlac,

'because they are wiser; knowledge will always predominate over ignorance, as man governs the other animals. But why their knowledge is more than ours, I know not what reason can be given, but the unsearchable will of the Supreme Being.'

'When,' said the prince with a sigh, 'shall I be able to visit Palestine, and mingle with this mighty confluence of nations? Till that happy moment shall arrive, let me fill up the time with such representations as thou canst give me. I am not ignorant of the motive that assembles such numbers in that place, and cannot but consider it as the centre of wisdom and piety, to which the best and wisest men of every land must be continually resorting.'

'There are some nations,' said Imlac, 'that send few visitants to Palestine ; for many numerous and learned sects in Europe concur to censure pilgrimage as superstitious, or deride it as ridiculous.'

'You know,' said the prince, 'how little my life has made me acquainted with diversity of opinions; it will be too long to hear the arguments on both sides; you, that have considered them, tell me the result.'

'Pilgrimage,' said Imlac, 'like many other acts of piety, may be reasonable or superstitious, according to the principles upon which it is performed. Long journeys in search of truth are not commanded. Truth, such as is necessary to the regulation of life, is always found where it is honestly sought. Change of place is no natural cause of the increase of piety, for it inevitably produces dissipation of mind. Yet, since men go every day to view the fields where great actions have been performed, and return with stronger impressions of the event, curiosity of the same kind may naturally dispose us to view that country whence our religion had its beginning; and I believe no man surveys those awful scenes without some confirmation of holy resolutions. That the

Supreme Being may be more easily propitiated in one place than in another, is the dream of idle superstition; but that some places may operate upon our own minds in an uncommon manner, is an opinion which hourly experience will justify. He who supposes that his vices may be more successfully combated in Palestine, will, perhaps, find himself mistaken; yet he may go thither without folly: he who thinks they will be more freely pardoned, dishonours at once his reason and religion.'

10   'These,' said the prince, 'are European distinctions. I will consider them another time. What have you found to be the effect of knowledge? Are those nations happier than we?'

'There is so much infelicity,' said the poet, 'in the world, that scarce any man has leisure from his own distresses to estimate the comparative happiness of others. Knowledge is certainly one of the means of pleasure, as is confessed by the natural desire which every mind feels of increasing its ideas. Ignorance is mere privation, by which nothing can 20 be produced: it is a vacuity in which the soul sits motionless and torpid for want of attraction; and, without knowing why, we always rejoice when we learn, and grieve when we forget. I am therefore inclined to conclude, that if nothing counteracts the natural consequence of learning, we grow more happy as our minds take a wider range.'

'In enumerating the particular comforts of life, we shall find many advantages on the side of the Europeans. They cure wounds and diseases with which we languish and perish. We suffer inclemencies of weather which they can 30 obviate. They have engines for the despatch of many laborious works, which we must perform by manual industry. There is such communication between distant places, that one friend can hardly be said to be absent from another. Their policy removes all public inconveniences; they have roads cut through their mountains, and bridges laid upon their rivers.   And, if we descend to the privacies of life, their habitations are more commodious, and their possessions are more secure.'

'They are surely happy,' said the prince, ' who have all these conveniences, of which I envy none so much as the facility with which separated friends interchange their thoughts.'

'The Europeans,' answered Imlac, ' are less unhappy than we; but they are not happy.   Human life is every where a state in which much is to be endured, and little to be enjoyed.'

CHAPTER XII.

THE STORY OF IMLAC CONTINUED.

'I AM not yet willing,' said the prince, ' to suppose that happiness is so parsimoniously distributed to mortals; nor can believe but that, if I had the choice of life, I should be able to fill every day with pleasure.   I would injure no man, and should provoke no resentment; I would relieve every distress, and should enjoy the benedictions of gratitude. I would choose my friends among the wise, and my wife among the virtuous ; and therefore should be in no danger from treachery or unkindness.   My children should, by my care, be learned and pious, and would repay to my age what their childhood had received.   What would dare to molest him who might call on every side to thousands enriched by his bounty, or assisted by his power?   And why should not life glide quietly away in the soft reciprocation of protection and reverence?   All this may be done without the help of European refinements, which appear by their effects to be rather specious than useful.   Let us leave them, and pursue our journey.'

'From Palestine,' said Imlac, 'I passed through many regions of Asia; in the more civilised kingdoms as a trader, and among the barbarians of the mountains as a pilgrim. At last I began to long for my native country, that I might repose, after my travels and fatigues, in the places where I had spent my earliest years, and gladden my old companions with the recital of my adventures. Often did I figure to myself those with whom I had sported away the gay hours of dawning life, sitting round me in its evening,
10 wondering at my tales, and listening to my counsels.

'When this thought had taken possession of my mind, I considered every moment as wasted which did not bring me nearer to Abyssinia. I hastened into Egypt, and notwithstanding my impatience, was detained ten months in the contemplation of its ancient magnificence, and in inquiries after the remains of its ancient learning. I found in Cairo a mixture of all nations; some brought thither by the love of knowledge, some by the hope of gain, and many by the desire of living after their own manner without observation,
20 and of lying hid in the obscurity of multitudes: for in a city, populous as Cairo, it is possible to obtain at the same time the gratifications of society, and the secrecy of solitude.

'From Cairo I travelled to Suez, and embarked on the Red Sea, passing along the coast till I arrived at the port from which I had departed twenty years before. Here I joined myself to a caravan, and re-entered my native country.

'I now expected the caresses of my kinsmen, and the
30 congratulations of my friends, and was not without hope that my father, whatever value he had set upon riches, would own with gladness and pride a son who was able to add to the felicity and honour of the nation. But I was soon convinced that my thoughts were vain. My father had been dead fourteen years, having divided his wealth among my

brothers, who were removed to some other provinces. Of my companions, the greater part were in the grave; of the rest, some could with difficulty remember me, and some considered me as one corrupted by foreign manners.

'A man used to vicissitudes, is not easily dejected. I forgot, after a time, my disappointment, and endeavoured to recommend myself to the nobles of the kingdom; they admitted me to their tables, heard my story, and dismissed me. I opened a school, and was prohibited to teach. I then resolved to sit down in the quiet of domestic life, and addressed a lady that was fond of my conversation, but rejected my suit because my father was a merchant.

'Wearied at last with solicitation and repulses, I resolved to hide myself for ever from the world, and depend no longer on the opinion or caprice of others. I waited for the time when the gate of the *happy valley* should open, that I might bid farewell to hope and fear: the day came; my performance was distinguished with favour; and I resigned myself with joy to perpetual confinement.'

'Hast thou here found happiness at last?' said Rasselas. 'Tell me without reserve; art thou content with thy condition? or, dost thou wish to be again wandering and inquiring? All the inhabitants of this valley celebrate their lot, and at the annual visit of the emperor, invite others to partake of their felicity.'

'Great prince,' said Imlac, 'I shall speak the truth; I know not one of all your attendants, who does not lament the hour when he entered this retreat. I am less unhappy than the rest, because I have a mind replete with images, which I can vary and combine at pleasure. I can amuse my solitude by the renovation of the knowledge which begins to fade from my memory, and by recollection of the incidents of my past life. Yet all this ends in the sorrowful consideration, that my acquirements are now useless, and that none of my pleasures can be again enjoyed. The rest, whose minds have no impression but of the present moment, are either corroded by malignant passions, or sit stupid in the gloom of perpetual vacancy.'

' What passions can infest those,' said the prince, ' who have no rivals? We are in a place where impotence precludes malice, and where all envy is repressed by community of enjoyments.'

' There may be community,' said Imlac, ' of material possessions, but there can never be community of love or of esteem. It must happen that one will please more than another; he that knows himself despised, will always be envious; and still more envious and malevolent, if he is condemned to live in the presence of those who despise him. The invitations by which they allure others, to a state which they feel to be wretched, proceed from the natural malignity of hopeless misery. They are weary of themselves and of each other, and expect to find relief in new companions. They envy the liberty which their folly has forfeited, and would gladly see all mankind imprisoned like themselves.

' From this crime, however, I am wholly free. No man can say that he is wretched by my persuasion. I look with pity on the crowds who are annually soliciting admission to captivity, and wish that it were lawful for me to warn them of their danger.'

' My dear Imlac,' said the prince, ' I will open to thee my whole heart. I have long meditated an escape from the *happy valley.* I have examined the mountains on every side, but find myself insuperably barred: teach me the way to break my prison ; thou shalt be the companion of my flight, the guide of my rambles, the partner of my fortune, and my sole director in the *choice of life.*'

' Sir,' answered the poet, ' your escape will be difficult,

and, perhaps, you may soon repent your curiosity. The world, which you figure to yourself smooth and quiet as the lake in the valley, you will find a sea foaming with tempests, and boiling with whirlpools: you will be sometimes overwhelmed by the waves of violence, and sometimes dashed against the rocks of treachery. Amidst wrongs and frauds, competitions and anxieties, you will wish a thousand times for these seats of quiet, and willingly quit hope to be free from fear.'

'Do not seek to deter me from my purpose,' said the prince; 'I am impatient to see what thou hast seen; and, since thou art thyself weary of the valley, it is evident that thy former state was better than this. Whatever be the consequence of my experiment, I am resolved to judge with mine own eyes of the various conditions of men, and then to make deliberately my *choice of life*.'

'I am afraid,' said Imlac, 'you are hindered by stronger restraints than my persuasions; yet, if your determination is fixed, I do not counsel you to despair. Few things are impossible to diligence and skill.'

CHAPTER XIII.

RASSELAS DISCOVERS THE MEANS OF ESCAPE.

THE prince now dismissed his favourite to rest; but the narrative of wonders and novelties filled his mind with perturbation. He revolved all that he had heard, and prepared innumerable questions for the morning.

Much of his uneasiness was now removed. He had a friend to whom he could impart his thoughts, and whose experience could assist him in his designs. His heart was no longer condemned to swell with silent vexation. He thought that even the *happy valley* might be endured with such a companion, and that if they could range the world together, he should have nothing further to desire.

In a few days the water was discharged, and the ground dried. The prince and Imlac then walked out together, to converse without the notice of the rest. The prince, whose thoughts were always on the wing, as he passed by the gate, said, with a countenance of sorrow, 'Why art thou so strong, and why is man so weak?'

'Man is not weak,' answered his companion; 'knowledge is more than equivalent to force. The master of mechanics laughs at strength. I can burst the gate, but cannot do it secretly. Some other expedient must be tried.'

As they were walking on the side of the mountain, they observed that the coneys, which the rain had driven from their burrows, had taken shelter among the bushes, and formed holes behind them, tending upwards in an oblique line. 'It has been the opinion of antiquity,' said Imlac, 'that human reason borrowed many arts from the instinct of animals; let us, therefore, not think ourselves degraded by learning from the coney. We may escape by piercing the mountain in the same direction. We will begin where the summit hangs over the middle part, and labour upward till we shall issue up beyond the prominence.'

The eyes of the prince, when he heard this proposal, sparkled with joy. The execution was easy, and the success certain.

No time was now lost. They hastened early in the morning to choose a place proper for their mine. They clambered with great fatigue among crags and brambles, and returned without having discovered any part that favoured their design. The second and the third day were spent in the same manner, and with the same frustration. But, on the fourth, they found a small cavern, concealed by a thicket, where they resolved to make their experiment.

Imlac procured instruments proper to hew stone and remove earth, and they fell to their work on the next day with more eagerness than vigour: they were presently exhausted by their efforts, and sat down to pant upon the grass. The prince, for a moment, appeared to be discouraged. 'Sir,' said his companion, 'practice will enable us to continue our labour for a longer time ; mark, however, how far we have advanced, and you will find that our toil will some time have an end. Great works are performed, not by strength, but perseverance : yonder palace was raised by single stones, yet you see its height and spaciousness. He that shall walk with vigour three hours a day, will pass in seven years a space equal to the circumference of the globe.'

They returned to their work day after day, and, in a short time, found a fissure in the rock, which enabled them to pass far with very little obstruction. This Rasselas considered as a good omen. 'Do not disturb your mind,' said Imlac, 'with other hopes or fears than reason may suggest : if you are pleased with prognostics of good, you will be terrified likewise with tokens of evil, and your whole life will be a prey to superstition. Whatever facilitates our work is more than an omen, it is a cause of success. This is one of those pleasing surprises which often happen to active resolution. Many things difficult to design prove easy to performance.'

CHAPTER XIV.

RASSELAS AND IMLAC RECEIVE AN UNEXPECTED VISIT.

They had now wrought their way to the middle, and solaced their toil with the approach of liberty, when the prince, coming down to refresh himself with air, found his sister Nekayah standing before the mouth of the cavity. He started and stood confused, afraid to tell his design, and yet hopeless to conceal it. A few moments determined him to repose on her fidelity, and secure her secrecy by a declaration without reserve.

'Do not imagine,' said the princess, 'that I came hither as a spy: I had long observed from my window that you and Imlac directed your walk every day towards the same point; but I did not suppose that you had any better reason for the preference than a cooler shade, or more fragrant bank; nor followed you with any other design than to partake of your conversation. Since, then, not suspicion but fondness has detected you, let me not lose the advantage of my discovery. I am equally weary of confinement with yourself, and not less desirous of knowing what is done or suffered in the world. Permit me to fly with you from this tasteless tranquillity, which will yet grow more loathsome when you have left me. You may deny me to accompany you, but cannot hinder me from following.'

The prince, who loved Nekayah above his other sisters, had no inclination to refuse her request, and grieved that he had lost an opportunity of showing his confidence by a voluntary communication. It was therefore agreed that she should leave the valley with them; and that, in the mean time, she should watch lest any other straggler should, by chance or curiosity, follow them to the mountain.

At length their labour was at an end; they saw light beyond the prominence, and, issuing to the top of the mountain, beheld the Nile, yet a narrow current, wandering beneath them.

The prince looked round with rapture, anticipated all the pleasure of travel, and in thought was already transported beyond his father's dominions. Imlac, though very joyful at his escape, had less expectation of pleasure in the world.

which he had before tried, and of which he had been weary

Rasselas was so much delighted with a wider horizon, that he could not soon be persuaded to return into the valley. He informed his sister that the way was open, and that nothing now remained but to prepare for their departure.

CHAPTER XV.

THE PRINCE AND PRINCESS LEAVE THE VALLEY, AND SEE MANY WONDERS.

1C

THE prince and princess had jewels sufficient to make them rich, whenever they came into a place of commerce, which, by Imlac's direction, they hid in their clothes; and, on the night of the next full moon, all left the valley. The princess was followed only by a single favourite, who did not know whither she was going.

They clambered through the cavity, and began to go down on the other side. The princess and her maid turned their eyes towards every part, and, seeing nothing to bound their prospect, considered themselves as in danger of being lost 20 in a dreary vacuity. They stopped and trembled. 'I am almost afraid,' said the princess, 'to begin a journey of which I cannot perceive an end, and to venture into this immense plain, where I may be approached on every side by men whom I never saw.' The prince felt nearly the same emotions, though he thought it more manly to conceal them.

Imlac smiled at their terrors, and encouraged them to proceed; but the princess continued irresolute till she had been imperceptibly drawn forward too far to return. 3C

In the morning they found some shepherds in the field, who set milk and fruits before them. The princess wondered that she did not see a palace ready for her reception, and a table spread with delicacies; but being faint and hungry, she drank the milk and ate the fruits, and thought them of a higher flavour than the products of the valley.

They travelled forward by easy journeys, being all unaccustomed to toil or difficulty, and knowing, that, though they might be missed, they could not be pursued. In a few days they came into a more populous region, where Imlac was diverted with the admiration which his companions expressed at the diversity of manners, stations, and employments.

Their dress was such as might not bring upon them the suspicion of having any thing to conceal; yet the prince, wherever he came, expected to be obeyed, and the princess was frighted because those that came into her presence did not prostrate themselves before her. Imlac was forced to observe them with great vigilance, lest they should betray their rank by their unusual behaviour, and detained them several weeks in the first village, to accustom them to the sight of common mortals.

By degrees the royal wanderers were taught to understand that they had for a time laid aside their dignity, and were to expect only such regard as liberality and courtesy could procure. And Imlac having, by many admonitions, prepared them to endure the tumults of a port, and the ruggedness of the commercial race, brought them down to the sea-coast.

The prince and his sister, to whom every thing was new, were gratified equally at all places, and therefore remained for some months at the port, without any inclination to pass further. Imlac was content with their stay, because he did not think it safe to expose them, unpractised in the world, to the hazards of a foreign country.

At last he began to fear lest they should be discovered, and proposed to fix a day for their departure. They had no pretensions to judge for themselves, and referred the whole scheme to his direction. He therefore took passage in a ship to Suez; and, when the time came, with great difficulty prevailed on the princess to enter the vessel. They had a quick and prosperous voyage, and from Suez travelled by land to Cairo.

CHAPTER XVI.

THEY ENTER CAIRO, AND FIND EVERY MAN HAPPY.

As they approached the city, which filled the strangers with astonishment, 'This,' said Imlac to the prince, 'is the place where travellers and merchants assemble from all the corners of the earth. You will here find men of every character, and every occupation. Commerce is here honourable: I will act as a merchant, and you shall live as strangers who have no other end of travel than curiosity; it will soon be observed that we are rich; our reputation will procure us access to all whom we shall desire to know; you will see all the conditions of humanity, and enable yourself at leisure to make your *choice of life.'*

They now entered the town, stunned by the noise, and offended by the crowds. Instruction had not yet so prevailed over habit, but that they wondered to see themselves pass undistinguished along the street, and met by the lowest of the people without reverence or notice. The princess could not at first bear the thought of being levelled with the vulgar, and for some days continued in her chamber, where she was served by her favourite Pekuah as in the palace of the valley.

Imlac, who understood traffic, sold part of the jewels the next day, and hired a house, which he adorned with such magnificence, that he was immediately considered as a merchant of great wealth. His politeness attracted many acquaintance, and his generosity made him courted by many dependents. His table was crowded by men of every nation, who all admired his knowledge, and solicited his favour. His companions, not being able to mix in the conversation, could make no discovery of their ignorance or surprise, and were gradually initiated in the world as they gained knowledge of the language.

10   The prince had, by frequent lectures, been taught the use and nature of money ; but the ladies could not, for a long time, comprehend what the merchants did with small pieces of gold and silver, or why things of so little use should be received as equivalent to the necessaries of life.

They studied the language two years, while Imlac was preparing to set before them the various ranks and conditions of mankind. He grew acquainted with all who had any thing uncommon in their fortune or conduct. He frequented the voluptuous and the frugal, the idle and the busy, the 20 merchants and the men of learning.

The prince being now able to converse with fluency, and having learned the caution necessary to be observed in his intercourse with strangers, began to accompany Imlac to places of resort, and to enter into all assemblies, that he might make his *choice of life*.

For some time he thought choice needless, because all appeared to him equally happy. Wherever he went he met gaiety and kindness, and heard the song of joy or the laugh of carelessness. He began to believe that the world 30 overflowed with universal plenty, and that nothing was withheld either from want or merit ; that every hand showered liberality, and every heart melted with benevolence ; 'and who then,' says he, 'will be suffered to be wretched ?'

Imlac permitted the pleasing delusion, and was unwilling to crush the hope of inexperience, till one day, having sat awhile silent, 'I know not,' said the prince, 'what can be the reason that I am more unhappy than any of our friends. I see them perpetually and unalterably cheerful, but feel my own mind restless and uneasy. I am unsatisfied with those pleasures which I seem most to court. I live in the crowds of jollity, not so much to enjoy company as to shun myself, and am only loud and merry to conceal my sadness.'

'Every man,' said Imlac, 'may, by examining his own mind, guess what passes in the minds of others; when you feel that your own gaiety is counterfeit, it may justly lead you to suspect that of your companions not to be sincere. Envy is commonly reciprocal. We are long before we are convinced that happiness is never to be found; and each believes it possessed by others, to keep alive the hope of obtaining it for himself. In the assembly where you passed the last night, there appeared such sprightliness of air and volatility of fancy, as might have suited beings of a higher order, formed to inhabit serener regions inaccessible to care or sorrow; yet, believe me, prince, there was not one who did not dread the moment when solitude should deliver him to the tyranny of reflexion.'

'This,' said the prince, 'may be true of others, since it is true of me; yet, whatever be the general infelicity of man, one condition is more happy than another, and wisdom surely directs us to take the least evil in the *choice of life.*'

'The causes of good and evil,' answered Imlac, 'are so various and uncertain, so often entangled with each other, so diversified by various relations, and so much subject to accidents which cannot be foreseen, that he who would fix his condition upon incontestable reasons of preference, must live and die inquiring and deliberating.'

'But surely,' said Rasselas, 'the wise men, to whom we listen with reverence and wonder, chose that mode of life for themselves which they thought most likely to make them happy.'

'Very few,' said the poet, 'live by choice. Every man is placed in his present condition by causes which acted without his foresight, and with which he did not always willingly co-operate; and therefore you will rarely meet one who does not think the lot of his neighbour better than his own.'

'I am pleased to think,' said the prince, 'that my birth has given me at least one advantage over others, by enabling me to determine for myself. I have here the world before me; I will review it at leisure: surely happiness is somewhere to be found.'

CHAPTER XVII.

THE PRINCE ASSOCIATES WITH YOUNG MEN OF SPIRIT AND GAIETY.

RASSELAS rose next day, and resolved to begin his experiments upon life. 'Youth,' cried he, 'is the time of gladness: I will join myself to the young men whose only business is to gratify their desires, and whose time is all spent in a succession of enjoyments.'

To such societies he was readily admitted; but a few days brought him back weary and disgusted. Their mirth was without images; their laughter without motive; their pleasures were gross and sensual, in which the mind had no part. Their conduct was at once wild and mean : they laughed at order and at law; but the frown of power dejected, and the eye of wisdom abashed them.

The prince soon concluded that he should never be happy

in a course of life of which he was ashamed. He thought it unsuitable to a reasonable being to act without a plan, and to be sad or cheerful only by chance. 'Happiness,' said he, 'must be something solid and permanent, without fear and without uncertainty.'

But his young companions had gained so much of his regard by their frankness and courtesy, that he could not leave them without warning and remonstrance. 'My friends,' said he, 'I have seriously considered our manners and our prospects, and find that we have mistaken our own interest. The first years of man must make provision for the last. He that never thinks never can be wise. Perpetual levity must end in ignorance ; and intemperance, though it may fire the spirits for an hour, will make life short or miserable. Let us consider that youth is of no long duration, and that in maturer age, when the enchantments of fancy shall cease, and phantoms of delight dance no more about us, we shall have no comforts but the esteem of wise men, and the means of doing good. Let us, therefore, stop, while to stop is in our power : let us live as men who are sometime to grow old, and to whom it will be the most dreadful of all evils to count their past years by follies, and to be reminded of their former luxuriance of health only by the maladies which riot has produced.'

They stared awhile in silence one upon another, and at last drove him away by a general chorus of continued laughter.

The consciousness that his sentiments were just, and his intentions kind, was scarcely sufficient to support him against the horror of derision. But he recovered his tranquillity, and pursued his search.

CHAPTER XVIII.

THE PRINCE FINDS A WISE AND HAPPY MAN.

As he was one day walking in the street, he saw a spacious building, which all were, by the open doors, invited to enter. He followed the stream of people, and found it a hall or school of declamation, in which professors read lectures to their auditory. He fixed his eye upon a sage raised above the rest, who discoursed with great energy on the government of the passions. His look was venerable, his action graceful, his pronunciation clear, and his diction elegant. He showed, with great strength of sentiment and variety of illustration, that human nature is degraded and debased when the lower faculties predominate over the higher; that when fancy, the parent of passion, usurps the dominion of the mind, nothing ensues but the natural effect of unlawful government,—perturbation and confusion; that she betrays the fortresses of the intellect to rebels, and excites her children to sedition against reason their lawful sovereign. He compared reason to the sun, of which the light is constant, uniform, and lasting; and fancy to a meteor, of bright but transitory lustre, irregular in its motion, and delusive in its direction.

He then communicated the various precepts given from time to time for the conquest of passion, and displayed the happiness of those who had obtained the important victory, after which man is no longer the slave of fear, nor the fool of hope; is no more emaciated by envy, inflamed by anger, emasculated by tenderness, or depressed by grief; but walks on calmly through the tumults or privacies of life, as the sun pursues alike his course through the calm or the stormy sky.

He enumerated many examples of heroes immovable by

pain or pleasure, who looked with indifference on those modes or accidents to which the vulgar give the names of good and evil. He exhorted his hearers to lay aside their prejudices, and arm themselves against the shafts of malice or misfortune, by invulnerable patience ; concluding, that this state only was happiness, and that this happiness was in every one's power.

Rasselas listened to him with the veneration due to the instructions of a superior being, and waiting for him at the door, humbly implored the liberty of visiting so great a master of true wisdom. The lecturer hesitated a moment, when Rasselas put a purse of gold into his hand, which he received with a mixture of joy and wonder.

'I have found,' said the prince at his return to Imlac, 'a man who can teach all that is necessary to be known, who, from the unshaken throne of rational fortitude, looks down on the scenes of life changing beneath him. He speaks, and attention watches his lips ; he reasons, and conviction closes his periods. This man shall be my future guide : I will learn his doctrines, and imitate his life.'

'Be not too hasty,' said Imlac, ' to trust or to admire the teachers of morality : they discourse like angels, but they live like men.'

Rasselas, who could not conceive how any man could reason so forcibly without feeling the cogency of his own arguments, paid his visit in a few days, and was denied admission. He had now learned the power of money, and made his way by a piece of gold to the inner apartment, where he found the philosopher, in a room half darkened, with his eyes misty, and his face pale. 'Sir,' said he, ' you are come at a time when all human friendship is useless : what I suffer cannot be remedied ; what I have lost cannot be supplied. My daughter, my only daughter, from whose tenderness I expected all the comforts of my age, died last night of a fever. My views, my purposes, my hopes are at an end: I am now a lonely being disunited from society.'

'Sir,' said the prince, 'mortality is an event by which a wise man can never be surprised: we know that death is always near, and it should therefore always be expected.'

'Young man,' answered the philosopher, 'you speak like one that has never felt the pangs of separation.' 'Have you then forgot the precepts,' said Rasselas, 'which you so powerfully enforced? Has wisdom no strength to arm the heart against calamity? Consider that external things are naturally variable, but truth and reason are always the same.' 'What comfort,' said the mourner, 'can truth and reason afford me? Of what effect are they now, but to tell me that my daughter will not be restored?'

The prince, whose humanity would not suffer him to insult misery with reproof, went away convinced of the emptiness of rhetorical sound, and the inefficacy of polished periods and studied sentences.

CHAPTER XIX.

A GLIMPSE OF PASTORAL LIFE.

HE was still eager upon the same inquiry; and having heard of a hermit, that lived near the lowest cataract of the Nile, and filled the whole country with the fame of his sanctity, resolved to visit his retreat, and inquire whether that felicity which public life could not afford, was to be found in solitude ; and whether a man whose age and virtue made him venerable, could teach any peculiar art of shunning evils or enduring them.

Imlac and the princess agreed to accompany him; and, after the necessary preparations, they began their journey. Their way lay through the fields, where shepherds tended their flocks, and the lambs were playing upon the pasture. 'This,' said the poet,' is the life which has been often celebrated for its innocence and quiet ; let us pass the heat of the day among the shepherds' tents, and know whether all our searches are not to terminate in pastoral simplicity.'

The proposal pleased them, and they induced the shepherds, by small presents and familiar questions, to tell their opinion of their own state. They were so rude and ignorant, so little able to compare the good with the evil of the occupation, and so indistinct in their narratives and descriptions, that very little could be learned from them ; but it was evident that their hearts were cankered with discontent, that they considered themselves as condemned to labour for the luxury of the rich, and looked up with stupid malevolence toward those that were placed above them.

The princess pronounced with vehemence, that she would never suffer these envious savages to be her companions, and that she should not soon be desirous of seeing any more specimens of rustic happiness ; but could not believe that all the accounts of primeval pleasures were fabulous, and was yet in doubt, whether life had any thing that could be justly preferred to the placid gratifications of fields and woods. She hoped that the time would come, when, with a few virtuous and elegant companions, she should gather flowers planted by her own hand, fondle the lambs of her own ewe, and listen without care, among brooks and breezes, to one of her maidens reading in the shade.

CHAPTER XX.

THE DANGER OF PROSPERITY.

On the next day they continued their journey, till the heat compelled them to look round for shelter. At a small

distance they saw a thick wood, which they no sooner entered
than they perceived that they were approaching the habitations of men.   The shrubs were diligently cut away, to open
walks where the shades were darkest ; the boughs of opposite trees were artificially interwoven ; seats of flowery turf
were raised in vacant spaces ; and a rivulet, that wantoned
along the side of a winding path, had its banks sometimes
opened into small basins, and its stream sometimes obstructed
by little mounds of stone, heaped together to increase its
10 murmurs.

They passed slowly through the wood, delighted with such
unexpected accommodations, and entertained each other
with conjecturing what or who he could be, that, in those
rude and unfrequented regions, had leisure and art for such
harmless luxury.

As they advanced, they heard the sound of music, and
saw youths and virgins dancing in the grove ; and going
still further, beheld a stately palace built upon a hill, surrounded with woods. The laws of eastern hospitality allowed
20 them to enter, and the master welcomed them like a man
liberal and wealthy.

He was skilful enough in appearances soon to discern
that they were no common guests, and spread his table
with magnificence.   The eloquence of Imlac caught his
attention, and the lofty courtesy of the princess excited his
respect.   When they offered to depart, he entreated their
stay, and was the next day still more unwilling to dismiss
them than before.   They were easily persuaded to stop, and
civility grew up in time to freedom and confidence.

30   The prince now saw all the domestics cheerful, and all
the face of nature smiling round the place, and could not
forbear to hope he should find here what he was seeking ;
but when he was congratulating the master upon his possessions, he answered with a sigh, ' My condition has indeed

the appearance of happiness, but appearances are delusive. My prosperity puts my life in danger; the Bassa of Egypt is my enemy, incensed only by my wealth and popularity. I have been hitherto protected against him by the princes of the country; but as the favour of the great is uncertain, I know not how soon my defenders may be persuaded to share the plunder with the Bassa. I have sent my treasures into a distant country, and, upon the first alarm, am prepared to follow them. Then will my enemies riot in my mansion, and enjoy the gardens which I have planted.'   10

They all joined in lamenting his danger, and deprecating his exile; and the princess was so much disturbed with the tumult of grief and indignation, that she retired to her apartment.

They continued with their kind inviter a few days longer, and then went forward to find the hermit.

CHAPTER XXI.

THE HAPPINESS OF SOLITUDE.   THE HERMIT'S HISTORY.

THEY came on the third day, by the direction of the peasants, to the hermit's cell: it was a cavern in the side 20 of a mountain, overshadowed with palm trees; at such a distance from the cataract, that nothing more was heard than a gentle uniform murmur, such as composed the mind to pensive meditation, especially when it was assisted by the wind whistling among the branches. The first rude essay of nature had been so much improved by human labour, that the cave contained several apartments appropriated to different uses, and often afforded lodging to travellers, whom darkness or tempests happened to overtake.

The hermit sat on a bench at the door, to enjoy the 30

coolness of the evening. On one side lay a book with pens and papers, on the other mechanical instruments of various kinds. As they approached him unregarded, the princess observed that he had not the countenance of a man that had found, or could teach, the way to happiness.

They saluted him with great respect, which he repaid like a man not unaccustomed to the forms of courts. 'My children,' said he, 'if you have lost your way, you shall be willingly supplied with such conveniences for the night as this cavern will afford. I have all that nature requires, and you will not expect delicacies in a hermit's cell.'

They thanked him, and, entering, were pleased with the neatness and regularity of the place. The hermit set flesh and wine before them, though he fed only upon fruits and water. His discourse was cheerful without levity, and pious without enthusiasm. He soon gained the esteem of his guests, and the princess repented of her hasty censure.

At last Imlac began thus: 'I do not now wonder that your reputation is so far extended. We have heard at Cairo of your wisdom, and came hither to implore your direction for this young man and maiden in the *choice of life.*'

'To him that lives well,' answered the hermit, 'every form of life is good; nor can I give any other rule for choice, than to remove from all apparent evil.'

'He will remove most certainly from evil,' said the prince, 'who shall devote himself to that solitude which you have recommended by your example.'

'I have indeed lived fifteen years in solitude,' said the hermit, 'but have no desire that my example should gain any imitators. In my youth I professed arms, and was raised by degrees to the highest military rank. I have traversed wide countries at the head of my troops, and seen many battles and sieges. At last, being disgusted by the preferments of a younger officer, and feeling that my vigour was beginning to decay, I was resolved to close my life in peace, having found the world full of snares, discord, and misery. I had once escaped from the pursuit of the enemy by the shelter of this cavern, and therefore chose it for my final residence. I employed artificers to form it into chambers, and stored it with all that I was likely to want.

'For some time after my retreat, I rejoiced like a tempest-beaten sailor at his entrance into the harbour, being delighted with the sudden change of the noise and hurry of war to stillness and repose. When the pleasure of novelty went away, I employed my hours in examining the plants which grow in the valley, and the minerals which I collected from the rocks. But that inquiry is now grown tasteless and irksome. I have been for some time unsettled and distracted: my mind is disturbed with a thousand perplexities of doubt and vanities of imagination, which hourly prevail upon me, because I have no opportunities of relaxation or diversion. I am sometimes ashamed to think that I could not secure myself from vice, but by retiring from the exercise of virtue, and begin to suspect that I was rather impelled by resentment, than led by devotion, into solitude. My fancy riots in scenes of folly, and I lament that I have lost so much and have gained so little. In solitude, if I escape the example of bad men, I want likewise the counsel and conversation of the good. I have been long comparing the evils with the advantages of society, and resolve to return into the world to-morrow. The life of a solitary man will be certainly miserable, but not certainly devout.'

They heard his resolution with surprise, but after a short pause, offered to conduct him to Cairo. He dug up a considerable treasure which he had hid among the rocks, and accompanied them to the city, on which, as he approached it, he gazed with rapture.

CHAPTER XXII.

THE HAPPINESS OF A LIFE LED ACCORDING TO NATURE.

RASSELAS went often to an assembly of learned men, who met at stated times to unbend their minds, and compare their opinions. Their manners were somewhat coarse, but their conversation was instructive, and their disputations acute, though sometimes too violent, and often continued till neither controvertist remembered upon what question they began. Some faults were almost general among them : every one was desirous to dictate to the rest, and every one was pleased to hear the genius or knowledge of another depreciated.

In this assembly Rasselas was relating his interview with the hermit, and the wonder with which he heard him censure a course of life which he had so deliberately chosen, and so laudably followed. The sentiments of the hearers were various. Some were of opinion, that the folly of his choice had been justly punished by condemnation to perpetual perseverance. One of the youngest among them, with great vehemence, pronounced him a hypocrite. Some talked of the right of society to the labour of individuals, and considered retirement as a desertion of duty. Others readily allowed that there was a time when the claims of the public were satisfied, and when a man might properly sequester himself, to review his life, and purify his heart.

One, who appeared more affected with the narrative than the rest, thought it likely that the hermit would, in a few years, go back to his retreat, and perhaps, if shame did not restrain or death intercept him, return once more from his retreat into the world : 'For the hope of happiness,' said he, 'is so strongly impressed, that the longest experience is not able to efface it. Of the present state, whatever it be, we feel, and are forced to confess, the misery; yet, when the same state is again at a distance, imagination paints it as desirable. But the time will surely come, when desire will be no longer our torment, and no man shall be wretched but by his own fault.

'This,' said a philosopher, who had heard him with tokens of great impatience, 'is the present condition of a wise man. The time is already come, when none are wretched but by their own fault. Nothing is more idle than to inquire after happiness, which nature has kindly placed within our reach. The way to be happy is to live according to nature, in obedience to that universal and unalterable law with which every heart is originally impressed; which is not written on it by precept, but engraven by destiny, not instilled by education, but infused at our nativity. He that lives according to nature will suffer nothing from the delusions of hope, or importunities of desire; he will receive and reject with equability of temper, and act or suffer as the reason of things shall alternately prescribe. Other men may amuse themselves with subtle definitions, or intricate ratiocinations. Let them learn to be wise by easier means: let them observe the hind of the forest, and the linnet of the grove; let them consider the life of animals, whose motions are regulated by instinct: they obey their guide, and are happy. Let us therefore, at length, cease to dispute, and learn to live; throw away the encumbrance of precepts, which they who utter them with so much pride and pomp do not understand, and carry with us this simple and intelligible maxim,—that deviation from nature is deviation from happiness.'

When he had spoken, he looked round him with a placid air, and enjoyed the consciousness of his own beneficence. 'Sir,' said the prince with great modesty, 'as I, like all the rest of mankind, am desirous of felicity, my closest attention has been fixed upon your discourse; I doubt not the truth of a position which a man so learned has so confidently advanced :—let me only know what it is to live according to nature.'

'When I find young men so humble and so docile,' said the philosopher, 'I can deny them no information which my studies have enabled me to afford.—To live according to nature, is to act always with due regard to the fitness arising from the relations and qualities of causes and effects ; to concur with the great and unchangeable scheme of universal felicity; to co-operate with the general disposition and tendency of the present system of things.'

The prince soon found that this was one of the sages whom he should understand less as he heard him longer. He therefore bowed and was silent ; and the philosopher, supposing him satisfied, and the rest vanquished, rose up, and departed with the air of a man that had co-operated with the present system.

CHAPTER XXIII.

THE PRINCE AND HIS SISTER DIVIDE BETWEEN THEM THE
WORK OF OBSERVATION.

RASSELAS returned home full of reflections, doubtful how to direct his future steps. Of the way to happiness he found the learned and simple equally ignorant ; but, as he was yet young, he flattered himself that he had time remaining for more experiments and further inquiries. He communicated to Imlac his observations and his doubts, but was answered by him with new doubts, and remarks that gave him no comfort. He therefore discoursed more frequently and freely with his sister, who had yet the same hope with himself, and always assisted him to give some reason why, though he had been hitherto frustrated, he might succeed at last.

'We have hitherto,' said she, 'known but little of the world: we have never yet been either great or mean. In our own country, though we had royalty, we had no power; and in this, we have not yet seen the private recesses of domestic peace. Imlac favours not our search, lest we should in time find him mistaken. We will divide the task between us: you shall try what is to be found in the splendour of courts, and I will range the shades of humbler life. Perhaps command and authority may be the supreme blessings, as they afford most opportunities of doing good; or, perhaps, what this world can give may be found in the modest habitations of middle fortune, too low for great designs, and too high for penury and distress.'

CHAPTER XXIV.

THE PRINCE EXAMINES THE HAPPINESS OF HIGH STATIONS.

RASSELAS applauded the design, and appeared next day with a splendid retinue at the court of the Bassa. He was soon distinguished for his magnificence, and admitted, as a prince whose curiosity had brought him from distant countries, to an intimacy with the great officers, and frequent conversation with the Bassa himself.

He was at first inclined to believe, that the man must be pleased with his own condition whom all approached with reverence and heard with obedience, and who had the power to extend his edicts to a whole kingdom. 'There can be no pleasure,' said he, 'equal to that of feeling at once the joy of thousands all made happy by wise administration. Yet, since by the law of subordination this sublime delight can be in one nation but the lot of one, it is surely reasonable to think that there is some satisfaction more popular and accessible, and that millions can hardly be subjected to the will of a single man, only to fill his particular breast with incommunicable content.'

These thoughts were often in his mind, and he found no solution of the difficulty. But as presents and civilities gained him more familiarity, he found that almost every man who stood high in employment hated all the rest, and was hated by them, and that their lives were a continual succession of plots and detections, stratagems and escapes, faction and treachery. Many of those who surrounded the Bassa, were sent only to watch and report his conduct; every tongue was muttering censure, and every eye was searching for a fault.

At last the letters of revocation arrived, the Bassa was carried in chains to Constantinople, and his name was mentioned no more.

'What are we now to think of the prerogatives of power,' said Rasselas to his sister; 'is it without any efficacy to good? or, is the subordinate degree only dangerous, and the supreme safe and glorious? Is the Sultan the only happy man in his dominions? or, is the Sultan himself subject to the torments of suspicion and the dread of enemies?'

In a short time the second Bassa was deposed; the Sultan that had advanced him was murdered by the Janizaries, and his successor had other views and different favourites.

CHAPTER XXV.

THE PRINCESS PURSUES HER INQUIRY WITH MORE DILIGENCE THAN SUCCESS.

The princess, in the mean time, insinuated herself into many families; for there are few doors through which liberality, joined with good humour, cannot find its way. The daughters of many houses were airy and cheerful; but Nekayah had been too long accustomed to the conversation of Imlac and her brother, to be much pleased with childish levity, and prattle which had no meaning. She found their thoughts narrow, their wishes low, and their merriment often artificial. Their pleasures, poor as they were, could not be preserved pure, but were embittered by petty competitions and worthless emulation. They were always jealous of the beauty of each other; of a quality to which solicitude can 10 add nothing, and from which detraction can take nothing away. Many were in love with triflers like themselves, and many fancied that they were in love when in truth they were only idle. Their affection was not fixed on sense or virtue, and therefore seldom ended but in vexation. Their grief, however, like their joy, was transient; every thing floated in their mind unconnected with the past or future, so that one desire easily gave way to another, as a second stone cast into the water effaces and confounds the circles of the first.

With these girls she played as with inoffensive animals, 20 and found them proud of her countenance, and weary of her company.

But her purpose was to examine more deeply, and her affability easily persuaded the hearts that were swelling with sorrow to discharge their secrets in her ear; and those whom hope flattered, or prosperity delighted, often courted her to partake their pleasures.

The princess and her brother commonly met in the evening, in a private summer house on the bank of the Nile, and related to each other the occurrences of the day. As they 30 were sitting together, the princess cast her eyes upon the river that flowed before her. 'Answer,' said she, 'great Father of Waters, thou that rollest thy floods through eighty nations, to the invocations of the daughter of thy native king.

Tell me if thou waterest, through all thy course, a single habitation from which thou dost not hear the murmurs of complaint?'

'You are, then,' said Rasselas, 'not more successful in private houses, than I have been in courts.' 'I have, since the last partition of our provinces,' said the princess, 'enabled myself to enter familiarly into many families, where there was the fairest show of prosperity and peace, and know not one house that is not haunted by some fury that destroys their quiet.

'I did not seek ease among the poor, because I concluded that there it could not be found. But I saw many poor, whom I had supposed to live in affluence. Poverty has, in large cities, very different appearances: it is often concealed in splendour, and often in extravagance. It is the care of a very great part of mankind to conceal their indigence from the rest; they support themselves by temporary expedients, and every day is lost in contriving for the morrow.

'This, however, was an evil, which, though frequent, I saw with less pain, because I could relieve it. Yet some have refused my bounties; more offended with my quickness to detect their wants, than pleased with my readiness to succour them; and others, whose exigencies compelled them to admit my kindness, have never been able to forgive their benefactress. Many, however, have been sincerely grateful, without the ostentation of gratitude, or the hope of other favours.'

CHAPTER XXVI.

THE PRINCESS CONTINUES HER REMARKS UPON PRIVATE LIFE.

NEKAYAH, perceiving her brother's attention fixed, proceeded in her narrative.

'In families, where there is or is not poverty, there is commonly discord: if a kingdom be, as Imlac tells us, a great family, a family likewise is a little kingdom, torn with factions, and exposed to revolutions. An unpractised observer expects the love of parents and children to be constant and equal; but this kindness seldom continues beyond the years of infancy: in a short time the children become rivals to their parents; benefits are allayed by reproaches, and gratitude debased by envy.

'Parents and children seldom act in concert: each child endeavours to appropriate the esteem or fondness of the parents, and the parents, with yet less temptation, betray each other to their children; thus, some place their confidence in the father, and some in the mother, and by degrees the house is filled with artifices and feuds.

'The opinions of children and parents, of the young and the old, are naturally opposite, by the contrary effects of hope and despondence, of expectation and experience, without crime or folly on either side. The colours of life in youth and age appear different, as the face of nature in spring and winter. And how can children credit the assertions of parents, which their own eyes show them to be false?

'Few parents act in such a manner as much to enforce their maxims by the credit of their lives. The old man trusts wholly to slow contrivance and gradual progression; the youth expects to force his way by genius, vigour, and precipitance. The old man pays regard to riches, and the youth reverences virtue. The old man deifies prudence; the youth commits himself to magnanimity and chance. The young man, who intends no ill, believes that none is intended, and therefore acts with openness and candour; but his father, having suffered the injuries of fraud, is impelled to suspect, and too often allured to practise it. Age looks with anger on the temerity of youth, and youth with contempt on the scrupulosity of age. Thus parents and children, for the greatest part, live on to love less and less; and, if those whom nature has thus closely united are the torments of each other, where shall we look for tenderness and consolation?'

'Surely,' said the prince, 'you must have been unfortunate in your choice of acquaintance: I am unwilling to believe, that the most tender of all relations is thus impeded in its effects by natural necessity.'

'Domestic discord,' answered she, 'is not inevitably and fatally necessary; but yet it is not easily avoided. We seldom see that a whole family is virtuous; the good and evil cannot well agree; and the evil can yet less agree with one another; even the virtuous fall sometimes to variance, when their virtues are of different kinds, and tending to extremes. In general, those parents have most reverence who most deserve it; for he that lives well cannot be despised.

'Many other evils infest private life. Some are the slaves of servants whom they have trusted with their affairs. Some are kept in continual anxiety by the caprice of rich relations, whom they cannot please, and dare not offend. Some husbands are imperious, and some wives perverse: and, as it is always more easy to do evil than good, though the wisdom or virtue of one can very rarely make many happy, the folly or vice of one may often make many miserable.'

'If such be the general effect of marriage,' said the prince, 'I shall, for the future, think it dangerous to connect my interest with that of another, lest I should be unhappy by my partner's fault.'

'I have met,' said the princess, 'with many who live single for that reason; but I never found that their prudence ought to raise envy. They dream away their time without friendship, without fondness, and are driven to rid themselves of the day, for which they have no use, by childish amusements or vicious delights. They act as beings under the constant sense of some known inferiority, that fills their minds with rancour, and their tongues with censure. They are peevish at home, and malevolent abroad; and, as the outlaws of human nature, make it their business and their pleasure to disturb that society which debars them from its privileges. To live without feeling or exciting sympathy, to be fortunate without adding to the felicity of others, or afflicted without tasting the balm of pity, is a state more gloomy than solitude : 10 it is not retreat, but exclusion from mankind. Marriage has many pains, but celibacy has no pleasures.' *84372*

'What then is to be done?' said Rasselas; 'the more we inquire, the less we can resolve. Surely he is most likely to please himself that has no other inclination to regard.'

CHAPTER XXVII.

DISQUISITION UPON GREATNESS.

THE conversation had a short pause. The prince having considered his sister's observations, told her, that she had surveyed life with prejudice, and supposed misery where 20 she did not find it. 'Your narrative,' says he, 'throws yet a darker gloom upon the prospects of futurity; the predictions of Imlac were but faint sketches of the evils painted by Nekayah. I have been lately convinced that quiet is not the daughter of grandeur or of power : that her presence is not to be bought by wealth, nor enforced by conquest. It is evident, that as any man acts in a wider compass, he must be more exposed to opposition from enmity, or miscarriage from chance; whoever has many to please or to govern, must use the ministry of many agents, some of whom will 30 be wicked, and some ignorant; by some he will be misled, and by others betrayed. If he gratifies one he will offend another; those that are not favoured will think themselves injured; and, since favours can be conferred but upon few, the greater number will be always discontented.'

'The discontent,' said the princess, 'which is thus unreasonable, I hope that I shall always have spirit to despise, and you power to repress.'

'Discontent,' answered Rasselas, 'will not always be without reason, under the most just and vigilant administration of public affairs. None, however attentive, can always discover that merit which indigence or faction may happen to obscure; and none, however powerful, can always reward it. Yet he that sees inferior desert advanced above him, will naturally impute that preference to partiality or caprice; and, indeed, it can scarcely be hoped that any man, however magnanimous by nature, or exalted by condition, will be able to persist for ever in the fixed and inexorable justice of distribution : he will sometimes indulge his own affections, and sometimes those of his favourites; he will permit some to please him who can never serve him; he will discover in those whom he loves, qualities which in reality they do not possess ; and to those from whom he receives pleasure, he will in his turn endeavour to give it. Thus will recommendations sometimes prevail which were purchased by money, or by the more destructive bribery of flattery and servility.

'He that has much to do will do something wrong, and of that wrong must suffer the consequences; and, if it were possible that he should always act rightly, yet when such numbers are to judge of his conduct, the bad will censure and obstruct him by malevolence, and the good sometimes by mistake.

'The highest stations cannot therefore hope to be the

abodes of happiness, which I would willingly believe to
have fled from thrones and palaces to seats of humble
privacy and placid obscurity.   For what can hinder the
satisfaction, or intercept the expectations, of him whose
abilities are adequate to his employments, who sees with
his own eyes the whole circuit of his influence, who chooses
by his own knowledge all whom he trusts, and whom none
are tempted to deceive by hope or fear? Surely he has
nothing to do but to love and to be loved, to be virtuous
and to be happy.'   10

'Whether perfect happiness would be procured by perfect
goodness,' said Nekayah, 'this world will never afford an
opportunity of deciding.   But this, at least, may be maintained, that we do not always find visible happiness in proportion to visible virtue.   All natural and almost all political
evils, are incident alike to the bad and good: they are con-
founded in the misery of a famine, and not much distinguished in the fury of a faction; they sink together in a
tempest, and are driven together from their country by invaders.   All that virtue can afford is quietness of conscience 20
and a steady prospect of a happier state; this may enable us
to endure calamity with patience; but remember that patience
must suppose pain.'

CHAPTER XXVIII.

RASSELAS AND NEKAYAH CONTINUE THEIR CONVERSATION.

'DEAR princess,' said Rasselas, 'you fall into the common errors of exaggeratory declamation, by producing, in
a familiar disquisition, examples of national calamities, and
scenes of extensive misery, which are found in books rather
than in the world, and which, as they are horrid, are ordained 30
to be rare.   Let us not imagine evils which we do not feel,

nor injure life by misrepresentations. I cannot bear that
querulous eloquence which threatens every city with a siege
like that of Jerusalem, that makes famine attend on every
flight of locusts, and suspends pestilence on the wing of
every blast that issues from the south.

'On necessary and inevitable evils which overwhelm kingdoms at once, all disputation is vain: when they happen
they must be endured. But it is evident, that these bursts
of universal distress are more dreaded than felt; thousands
and ten thousands flourish in youth and wither in age, without the knowledge of any other than domestic evils, and
share the same pleasures and vexations, whether their kings
are mild or cruel, whether the armies of their country pursue
their enemies or retreat before them. While courts are disturbed with intestine competitions, and ambassadors are
negotiating in foreign countries, the smith still plies his
anvil, and the husbandman drives his plough forward; the
necessaries of life are required and obtained; and the successive business of the seasons continues to make its wonted
revolutions.

'Let us cease to consider what, perhaps, may never happen, and what, when it shall happen, will laugh at human
speculation. We will not endeavour to modify the motions
of the elements, or to fix the destiny of kingdoms. It is our
business to consider what beings like us may perform; each
labouring for his own happiness, by promoting within his
circle, however narrow, the happiness of others.

'Marriage is evidently the dictate of nature; men and
women are made to be companions of each other; and
therefore I cannot be persuaded but that marriage is one of
the means of happiness.'

'I know not,' said the princess, 'whether marriage be
more than one of the innumerable modes of human misery.
When I see and reckon the various forms of connubial

infelicity, the unexpected causes of lasting discord, the diversities of temper, the oppositions of opinion, the rude collisions of contrary desire where both are urged by violent impulses, the obstinate contests of disagreeing virtues where both are supported by consciousness of good intention, I am sometimes disposed to think with the severer casuists of most nations, that marriage is rather permitted than approved, and that none, but by the instigation of a passion too much indulged, entangle themselves with indissoluble compacts.'   10

'You seem to forget,' replied Rasselas,' ' that you have, even now, represented celibacy as less happy than marriage. Both conditions may be bad, but they cannot both be worst. Thus it happens when wrong opinions are entertained, that they mutually destroy each other, and leave the mind open to truth.'

'I did not expect,' answered the princess, 'to hear that imputed to falsehood which is the consequence only of frailty. To the mind, as to the eye, it is difficult to compare with exactness objects vast in their extent, and various 20 in their parts. Where we see or conceive the whole at once, we readily note the discriminations, and decide the preference; but of two systems, of which neither can be surveyed by any human being in its full compass of magnitude and multiplicity of complication, where is the wonder, that, judging of the whole by parts, I am alternately affected by one and the other, as either presses on my memory or fancy? We differ from ourselves, just as we differ from each other, when we see only part of the question, as in the multifarious relations of politics and morality; but when we 30 perceive the whole at once, as in numerical computations, all agree in one judgment, and none ever varies his opinion.'

'Let us not add,' said the prince, ' to the other evils of life the bitterness of controversy, nor endeavour to vie with each other in subtilities of argument. We are employed in a search, of which both are equally to enjoy the success, or suffer by the miscarriage. It is therefore fit that we assist each other. You surely conclude too hastily from the infelicity of marriage against its institution: will not the misery of life prove equally that life cannot be the gift of heaven? The world must be peopled by marriage, or peopled without it.'

'How the world is to be peopled,' returned Nekayah, 'is not my care, and needs not be yours. I see no danger that the present generation should omit to leave successors behind them: we are not now inquiring for the world, but for ourselves.'

CHAPTER XXIX.

THE DEBATE OF MARRIAGE CONTINUED.

'The good of the whole,' says Rasselas, 'is the same with the good of all its parts. If marriage be best for mankind, it must be evidently best for individuals; or a permanent and necessary duty must be the cause of evil, and some must be inevitably sacrificed to the convenience of others. In the estimate which you have made of the two states, it appears that the incommodities of a single life are, in a great measure, necessary and certain, but those of the conjugal state accidental and avoidable.

'I cannot forbear to flatter myself, that prudence and benevolence will make marriage happy. The general folly of mankind is the cause of general complaint. What can be expected but disappointment and repentance from a choice made in the immaturity of youth, in the ardour of desire, without judgment, without foresight, without inquiry after conformity of opinions, similarity of manners, rectitude of judgment, or purity of sentiment?

' Such is the common process of marriage. A youth and maiden, meeting by chance or brought together by artifice, exchange glances, reciprocate civilities, go home, and dream of one another. Having little to divert attention, or diversify thought, they find themselves uneasy when they are apart, and therefore conclude that they shall be happy together. They marry, and discover what nothing but voluntary blindness before had concealed: they wear out life in altercations, 10 and charge nature with cruelty.

' From those early marriages proceeds likewise the rivalry of parents and children. The son is eager to enjoy the world before the father is willing to forsake it, and there is hardly room at once for two generations. The daughter begins to bloom before the mother can be content to fade, and neither can forbear to wish for the absence of the other.

' Surely all these evils may be avoided by that deliberation and delay which prudence prescribes to irrevocable choice. In the variety and jollity of youthful pleasures, life may be 20 well enough supported without the help of a partner. Longer time will increase experience, and wider views will allow better opportunities of inquiry and selection : one advantage, at least, will be certain ; the parents will be visibly older than their children.'

' What reason cannot collect,' said Nekayah, ' and what experiment has not yet taught, can be known only from the report of others. I have been told that late marriages are not eminently happy. This is a question too important to be neglected, and I have often proposed it to those whose 30 accuracy of remark, and comprehensiveness of knowledge, made their suffrages worthy of regard. They have generally determined that it is dangerous for a man and woman to suspend their fate upon each other, at a time when opinions

are fixed, and habits are established; when friendships have
been contracted on both sides; when life has been planned
into method, and the mind has long enjoyed the contemplation of its own prospects.

'It is scarcely possible that two travelling through the
world under the conduct of chance, should have been both
directed to the same path, and it will not often happen that
either will quit the track which custom has made pleasing.
When the desultory levity of youth has settled into regularity, it is soon succeeded by pride ashamed to yield, or
obstinacy delighting to contend. And even though mutual
esteem produces mutual desire to please, time itself, as it
modifies unchangeably the external mien, determines likewise the direction of the passions, and gives an inflexible
rigidity to the manners. Long customs are not easily
broken : he that attempts to change the course of his own
life, very often labours in vain : and how shall we do that
for others, which we are seldom able to do for ourselves?'

'But surely,' interposed the prince, 'you suppose the
chief motive of choice forgotten or neglected. Whenever
I shall seek a wife, it shall be my first question, whether she
be willing to be led by reason.'

'Thus it is,' said Nekayah, 'that philosophers are deceived. There are a thousand familiar disputes which
reason never can decide; questions that elude investigation,
and make logic ridiculous; cases where something must be
done, and where little can be said. Consider the state of
mankind, and inquire how few can be supposed to act upon
any occasions, whether small or great, with all the reasons
of action present to their minds. Wretched would be the
pair above all names of wretchedness, who should be
doomed to adjust by reason, every morning, all the minute
detail of a domestic day.

'Those who marry at an advanced age, will probably

escape the encroachments of their children; but, in diminution of this advantage, they will be likely to leave them, ignorant and helpless, to a guardian's mercy; or, if that should not happen, they must at least go out of the world before they see those whom they love best either wise or great.

'From their children, if they have less to fear, they have less also to hope, and they lose, without equivalent, the joys of early love, and the convenience of uniting with manners pliant, and minds susceptible of new impressions, which might wear away their dissimilitudes by long cohabitation, as soft bodies, by continual attrition, conform their surfaces to each other.

'I believe it will be found, that those who marry late are best pleased with their children, and those who marry early, with their partners.'

'The union of these two affections,' said Rasselas, ' would produce all that could be wished. Perhaps there is a time when marriage might unite them, a time neither too early for the father, nor too late for the husband.

'Every hour,' answered the princess, ' confirms my prejudice in favour of the position so often uttered by the mouth of Imlac,—That nature sets her gifts on the right hand and on the left. Those conditions which flatter hope and attract desire, are so constituted, that, as we approach one, we recede from another. There are goods so opposed that we cannot seize both, but, by too much prudence, may pass between them at too great a distance to reach either. This is often the fate of long consideration: he does nothing who endeavours to do more than is allowed to humanity. Flatter not yourself with contrarieties of pleasure. Of the blessings set before you, make your choice, and be content. No man can taste the fruits of autumn while he is delighting his scent with the flowers of the spring: no man can, at the

same time, fill his cup from the source and from the mouth
of the Nile.'

CHAPTER XXX.

IMLAC ENTERS AND CHANGES THE CONVERSATION.

HERE Imlac entered, and interrupted them. 'Imlac,'
said Rasselas, 'I have been taking from the princess the
dismal history of private life, and am almost discouraged
from further search.'

'It seems to me,' said Imlac, 'that while you are making
the choice of life, you neglect to live. You wander about
a single city, which, however large and diversified, can now
afford few novelties, and forget that you are in a country,
famous among the earliest monarchies for the power and
wisdom of its inhabitants; a country where the sciences first
dawned that illuminate the world, and beyond which the
arts cannot be traced of civil society or domestic life.

'The old Egyptians have left behind them monuments
of industry and power, before which all European magnificence is confessed to fade away. The ruins of their
architecture are the schools of modern builders, and from
the wonders which time has spared, we may conjecture,
though uncertainly, what it has destroyed.'

'My curiosity,' said Rasselas, 'does not very strongly
lead me to survey piles of stone, or mounds of earth; my
business is with man. I came hither not to measure frag-
ments of temples, or trace choked aqueducts, but to look
upon the various scenes of the present world.'

'The things that are now before us,' said the princess,
'require attention, and deserve it. What have I to do with
the heroes or the monuments of ancient times? with times
which never can return, and heroes whose form of life was

different from all that the present condition of mankind
requires or allows?'

'To know anything,' returned the poet, 'we must know
its effects; to see men we must see their works, that we may
learn what reason has dictated, or passion has incited, and
find what are the most powerful motives of action. To
judge rightly of the present, we must oppose it to the past;
for all judgment is comparative, and of the future nothing
can be known. The truth is, that no mind is much employed upon the present; recollection and anticipation fill 10
up almost all our moments. Our passions are joy and grief,
love and hatred, hope and fear. Of joy and grief the past is
the object, and the future of hope and fear: even love and
hatred respect the past, for the cause must have been before
the effect.

'The present state of things is the consequence of the
former, and it is natural to inquire what were the sources
of the good that we enjoy, or the evil that we suffer. If we
act only for ourselves, to neglect the study of history is not
prudent; if we are intrusted with the care of others, it is 20
not just. Ignorance, when it is voluntary, is criminal; and
he may properly be charged with evil, who refused to learn
how he might prevent it.

'There is no part of history so generally useful as that
which relates the progress of the human mind, the gradual
improvement of reason, the successive advances of science,
the vicissitudes of learning and ignorance, which are the
light and darkness of thinking beings, the extinction and
resuscitation of arts, and the revolutions of the intellectual
world. If accounts of battles and invasions are peculiarly 30
the business of princes, the useful or elegant arts are not to
be neglected; those who have kingdoms to govern, have
understandings to cultivate.

'Example is always more efficacious than precept. A

soldier is formed in war, and a painter must copy pictures. In this contemplative life has the advantage,—great actions are seldom seen, but the labours of art are always at hand, for those who desire to know what art has been able to perform.

'When the eye or the imagination is struck with an uncommon work, the next transition of an active mind is to the means by which it was performed. Here begins the true use of such contemplation; we enlarge our comprehension by new ideas, and perhaps recover some art lost to mankind, or learn what is less perfectly known in our own country. At least we compare our own with former times, and either rejoice at our improvements, or, what is the first motion towards good, discover our defects.'

'I am willing,' said the prince, 'to see all that can deserve my search.' 'And I,' said the princess, 'shall rejoice to learn something of the manners of antiquity.'

'The most pompous monument of Egyptian greatness, and one of the most bulky works of manual industry,' said Imlac, 'are the Pyramids; fabrics raised before the time of history, and of which the earliest narratives afford us only uncertain traditions. Of these the greatest is still standing, very little injured by time.'

'Let us visit them to-morrow,' said Nekayah. 'I have often heard of the Pyramids, and shall not rest till I have seen them within and without with my own eyes.'

CHAPTER XXXI.

THEY VISIT THE PYRAMIDS.

THE resolution being thus taken, they set out the next day. They laid tents upon their camels, being resolved to stay among the Pyramids till their curiosity was fully satisfied. They travelled gently, turned aside to everything remarkable, stopped from time to time and conversed with the inhabitants, and observed the various appearances of towns ruined and inhabited, of wild and cultivated nature.

When they came to the great Pyramid, they were astonished at the extent of the base, and the height of the top. Imlac explained to them the principles upon which the pyramidal form was chosen for a fabric intended to co-extend its duration with that of the world: he showed that its gradual diminution gave it such stability as defeated all the common attacks of the elements, and could scarcely be overthrown by earthquakes themselves, the least resistible of natural violence. A concussion that should shatter the Pyramid would threaten the dissolution of the continent.

They measured all its dimensions, and pitched their tents at its foot. Next day they prepared to enter its interior apartments, and having hired the common guides, climbed up to the first passage, when the favourite of the princess, looking into the cavity, stepped back and trembled. 'Pekuah,' said the princess, 'of what art thou afraid?' 'Of the narrow entrance,' answered the lady, 'and of the dreadful gloom. I dare not enter a place which must surely be inhabited by unquiet souls. The original possessors of these dreadful vaults will start up before us, and perhaps shut us in for ever.' She spoke, and threw her arms round the neck of her mistress.

'If all your fear be of apparitions,' said the prince, 'I will promise you safety: there is no danger from the dead: he that is once buried will be seen no more.'

'That the dead are seen no more,' said Imlac, 'I will not undertake to maintain, against the concurrent and unvaried testimony of all ages, and of all nations. There is no people, rude or learned, among whom apparitions of the dead are not related and believed. This opinion, which perhaps prevails as far as human nature is diffused, could become universal only by its truth: those that never heard of one another, would not have agreed in a tale which nothing but experience can make credible. That it is doubted by single cavillers, can very little weaken the general evidence; and some who deny it with their tongues, confess it by their fears.

'Yet I do not mean to add new terrors to those which have already seized upon Pekuah. There can be no reason why spectres should haunt the Pyramid more than other places, or why they should have power or will to hurt innocence and purity. Our entrance is no violation of their privileges; we can take nothing from them, how then can we offend them?'

'My dear Pekuah,' said the princess, 'I will always go before you, and Imlac shall follow you. Remember that you are the companion of the princess of Abyssinia.'

'If the princess is pleased that her servant should die,' returned the lady, 'let her command some death less dreadful than enclosure in this horrid cavern. You know I dare not disobey you: I must go if you command me; but, if I once enter, I never shall come back.'

The princess saw that her fear was too strong for expostulation or reproof, and embracing her, told her that she should stay in the tent till their return. Pekuah was yet not satisfied, but entreated the princess not to pursue so dreadful a purpose as that of entering the recesses of the Pyramid. 'Though I cannot teach courage,' said Nekayah, 'I must not learn cowardice; nor leave at last undone what I came hither only to do.'

CHAPTER XXXII.

THEY ENTER THE PYRAMID.

PEKUAH descended to the tents, and the rest entered the pyramid : they passed through the galleries, surveyed the vaults of marble, and examined the chest in which the body of the founder is supposed to have been reposited. They then sat down in one of the most spacious chambers to rest while before they attempted to return.

'We have now,' said Imlac, 'gratified our minds with an exact view of the greatest work of man, except the wall of 10 China.

'Of the wall it is very easy to assign the motive. It secured a wealthy and timorous nation from the incursions of barbarians, whose unskilfulness in arts made it easier for them to supply their wants by rapine than by industry, and who from time to time poured in upon the habitations of peaceful commerce, as vultures descend upon domestic fowl. Their celerity and fierceness made the wall necessary, and their ignorance made it efficacious.

'But for the Pyramids no reason has ever been given 20 adequate to the cost and labour of the work. The narrowness of the chambers proves that it could afford no retreat from enemies, and treasures might have been reposited at far less expense with equal security. It seems to have been erected only in compliance with that hunger of imagination which preys incessantly upon life, and must be always appeased by some employment. Those who have already all that they can enjoy, must enlarge their desires. He that has built for use, till use is supplied, must begin to build for vanity, and extend his plan to the utmost power of human 30

performance, that he may not be soon reduced to form
another wish.

'I consider this mighty structure as a monument of the
insufficiency of human enjoyments. A king whose power
is unlimited, and whose treasures surmount all real and
imaginary wants, is compelled to solace, by the erection
of a Pyramid, the satiety of dominion and tastelessness of
pleasures, and to amuse the tediousness of declining life, by
seeing thousands labouring without end, and one stone, for
10 no purpose, laid upon another. Whoever thou art that, not
content with a moderate condition, imaginest happiness in
royal magnificence, and dreamest that command or riches
can feed the appetite of novelty with perpetual gratifications,
survey the Pyramids, and confess thy folly!'

CHAPTER XXXIII.

THE PRINCESS MEETS WITH AN UNEXPECTED MISFORTUNE.

THEY rose up, and returned through the cavity at which
they had entered, and the princess prepared for her favourite
a long narrative of dark labyrinths and costly rooms, and of
20 the different impressions which the varieties of the way had
made upon her. But when they came to their train, they
found every one silent and dejected; the men discovered
shame and fear in their countenances, and the women were
weeping in the tents.

What had happened they did not try to conjecture, but
immediately inquired. 'You had scarcely entered into the
Pyramid,' said one of the attendants, 'when a troop of
Arabs rushed upon us; we were too few to resist them, and
too slow to escape. They were about to search the tents,
30 set us on our camels, and drive us along before them, when

he approach of some Turkish horsemen put them to flight; ut they seized the lady Pekuah with her two maids, and :arried them away. The Turks are now pursuing them by ur instigation, but I fear they will not be able to overtake hem.'

The princess was overpowered with surprise and grief. Rasselas, in the first heat of his resentment, ordered his servants to follow him, and prepared to pursue the robbers with his sabre in his hand. 'Sir,' said Imlac, 'what can you hope from violence or valour? the Arabs are mounted 10 on horses trained to battle and retreat; we have only beasts of burden. By leaving our present station we may lose the princess, but cannot hope to regain Pekuah.'

In a short time the Turks returned, having not been able to reach the enemy. The princess burst out into new lamentations, and Rasselas could scarcely forbear to reproach them with cowardice; but Imlac was of opinion that the escape of the Arabs was no addition to their misfortune, for perhaps they would have killed their captives rather than have resigned them. 20

CHAPTER XXXIV.

THEY RETURN TO CAIRO WITHOUT PEKUAH.

THERE was nothing to be hoped from longer stay. They returned to Cairo, repenting of their curiosity, censuring the negligence of the government, lamenting their own rashness which had neglected to procure a guard, imagining many expedients by which the loss of Pekuah might have been prevented, and resolving to do something for her recovery, though none could find any thing proper to be done.

Nekayah retired to her chamber, where her women 30 attempted to comfort her by telling her that all had their troubles, and that lady Pekuah had enjoyed much happiness in the world for a long time, and might reasonably expect a change of fortune. They hoped that some good would befall her wheresoever she was, and that their mistress would find another friend who might supply her place.

The princess made them no answer, and they continued the form of condolence, not much grieved in their hearts that the favourite was lost.

Next day the prince presented to the Bassa a memorial of the wrong which he had suffered, and a petition for redress. The Bassa threatened to punish the robbers, but did not attempt to catch them; nor indeed could any account or description be given by which he might direct the pursuit.

It soon appeared that nothing would be done by authority. Governors being accustomed to hear of more crimes than they can punish, and more wrongs than they can redress, set themselves at ease by indiscriminate negligence, and presently forget the request when they lose sight of the petitioner.

Imlac then endeavoured to gain some intelligence by private agents. He found many who pretended to an exact knowledge of all the haunts of the Arabs, and to regular correspondence with their chiefs, and who readily undertook the recovery of Pekuah. Of these, some were furnished with money for their journey, and came back no more; some were liberally paid for accounts which a few days discovered to be false. But the princess would not suffer any means, however improbable, to be left untried. While she was doing something, she kept her hope alive. As one expedient failed, another was suggested; when one messenger returned unsuccessful, another was despatched to a different quarter.

Two months had now passed, and of Pekuah nothing had

been neard; the hopes which they had endeavoured to raise
in each other grew more languid, and the princess when she
saw nothing more to be tried, sunk down inconsolable in
hopeless dejection. A thousand times she reproached herself with the easy compliance by which she permitted her
favourite to stay behind her. 'Had not my fondness,' said
she, 'lessened my authority, Pekuah had not dared to talk
of her terrors. She ought to have feared me more than
spectres. A severe look would have overpowered her; a
peremptory command would have compelled obedience. 10
Why did foolish indulgence prevail upon me? Why did I
not speak, and refuse to hear?'

'Great princess,' said Imlac, 'do not reproach yourself
for your virtue, or consider that as blamable by which evil
has accidentally been caused. Your tenderness for the
timidity of Pekuah was generous and kind. When we act
according to our duty, we commit the event to him by
whose laws our actions are governed, and who will suffer
none to be finally punished for obedience. When, in prospect of some good, whether natural or moral, we break the 20
rules prescribed us, we withdraw from the direction of superior wisdom, and take all consequences upon ourselves.
Man cannot so far know the connexion of causes and events,
as that he may venture to do wrong in order to do right.
When we pursue our end by lawful means, we may always
console our miscarriage by the hope of future recompense.
When we consult only our own policy, and attempt to find
a nearer way to good, by overleaping the settled boundaries
of right and wrong, we cannot be happy even by success,
because we cannot escape the consciousness of our fault: 30
but if we miscarry, the disappointment is irremediably embittered. How comfortless is the sorrow of him who feels
at once the pangs of guilt, and the vexation of calamity
which guilt has brought upon him!

'Consider, princess, what would have been your condition, if the lady Pekuah had entreated to accompany you, and being compelled to stay in the tents, had been carried away; or how would you have borne the thought, if you had forced her into the Pyramid, and she had died before you in agonies of terror.'

'Had either happened,' said Nekayah, 'I could not have endured life till now: I should have been tortured to madness by the remembrance of such cruelty, or must have pined away in abhorrence of myself.'

'This at least,' said Imlac, 'is the present reward of virtuous conduct, that no unlucky consequence can oblige us to repent it.'

CHAPTER XXXV.

THE PRINCESS LANGUISHES FOR WANT OF PEKUAH.

NEKAYAH being thus reconciled to herself, found that no evil is insupportable, but that which is accompanied with consciousness of wrong. She was from that time delivered from the violence of tempestuous sorrow, and sunk into silent pensiveness and gloomy tranquillity. She sat from morning to evening recollecting all that had been done or said by her Pekuah, treasured up with care every trifle on which Pekuah had set an accidental value, and which might recall to mind any little incident or careless conversation. The sentiments of her whom she now expected to see no more, were treasured in her memory as rules of life, and she deliberated to no other end than to conjecture, on any occasion, what would have been the opinion and counsel of Pekuah.

The women by whom she was attended knew nothing of her real condition, and therefore she could not talk to them but with caution and reserve. She began to remit her curiosity, having no great care to collect notions which she had no convenience of uttering. Rasselas endeavoured first to comfort, and afterwards to divert her; he hired musicians, to whom she seemed to listen, but did not hear them, and procured masters to instruct her in various arts, whose lectures, when they visited her again, were again to be repeated. She had lost her taste of pleasure, and her ambition of excellence. And her mind, though forced into short excursions, always recurred to the image of her friend. 10

Imlac was every morning earnestly enjoined to renew his inquiries, and was asked every night whether he had yet heard of Pekuah, till not being able to return the princess the answer that she desired, he was less and less willing to come into her presence. She observed his backwardness, and commanded him to attend her. 'You are not,' said she, ' to confound impatience with resentment, or to suppose that I charge you with negligence, because I repine at your unsuccessfulness. I do not much wonder at your absence; I know that the unhappy are never pleasing, and that all 20 naturally avoid the contagion of misery. To hear complaints is wearisome alike to the wretched and the happy; for who would cloud, by adventitious grief, the short gleams of gaiety which life allows us? or who that is struggling under his own evils, will add to them the miseries of another?

'The time is at hand, when none shall be disturbed any longer by the sighs of Nekayah; my search after happiness is now at an end. I am resolved to retire from the world with all its flatteries and deceits, and will hide myself in solitude, without any other care than to compose my thoughts, 30 and regulate my hours by a constant succession of innocent occupations, till with a mind purified from all earthly desires, I shall enter into that state to which all are hastening, and in which I hope again to enjoy the friendship of Pekuah.'

'Do not entangle your mind,' said Imlac, 'by irrevocable determinations, nor increase the burden of life by a voluntary accumulation of misery: the weariness of retirement will continue or increase when the loss of Pekuah is forgotten. That you have been deprived of one pleasure, is no very good reason for rejection of the rest.'

'Since Pekuah was taken from me,' said the princess, 'I have no pleasure to reject or to retain. She that has no one to love or trust has little to hope. She wants the radical principle of happiness. We may, perhaps, allow, that what satisfaction this world can afford, must arise from the conjunction of wealth, knowledge, and goodness: wealth is nothing but as it is bestowed, and knowledge nothing but as it is communicated; they must therefore be imparted to others, and to whom could I now delight to impart them? Goodness affords the only comfort which can be enjoyed without a partner, and goodness may be practised in retirement.'

'How far solitude may admit goodness or advance it, I shall not,' replied Imlac, 'dispute at present. Remember the confession of the pious hermit. You will wish to return into the world, when the image of your companion has left your thoughts.'—'That time,' said Nekayah, 'will never come. The generous frankness, the modest obsequiousness, and the faithful secrecy of my dear Pekuah, will always be more missed, as I shall live longer to see vice and folly.'

'The state of a mind oppressed with a sudden calamity,' said Imlac, 'is like that of the fabulous inhabitants of the new-created earth, who when the first night came upon them, supposed that day would never return. When the clouds of sorrow gather over us, we see nothing beyond them, nor can imagine how they will be dispelled; yet a new day succeeded to the night, and sorrow is never long without a dawn of ease. But they who restrain themselves from receiving comfort, do as the savages would have done, had they put out their eyes when it was dark. Our minds, like our bodies, are in continual flux; something is hourly lost, and something acquired. To lose much at once is inconvenient to either, but while the vital powers remain uninjured, nature will find the means of reparation. Distance has the same effect on the mind as on the eye, and while we glide along the stream of time, whatever we leave behind us is always lessening, and that which we approach increasing, in magnitude. Do not suffer life to stagnate; it will grow 10 muddy for want of motion; commit yourself again to the current of the world; Pekuah will vanish by degrees: you will meet in your way some other favourite, or learn to diffuse yourself in general conversation.'

'At least,' said the prince, 'do not despair before all remedies have been tried; the inquiry after the unfortunate lady is still continued, and shall be carried on with yet greater diligence, on condition that you will promise to wait a year for the event, without any unalterable resolution.'

Nekayah thought this a reasonable demand, and made 20 the promise to her brother, who had been advised by Imlac to require it. Imlac had, indeed, no great hope of regaining Pekuah; but he supposed, that if he could secure the interval of a year, the princess would be then in no danger of a cloister.

CHAPTER XXXVI.

PEKUAH IS STILL REMEMBERED. THE PROGRESS OF SORROW.

NEKAYAH, seeing that nothing was omitted for the recovery of her favourite, and having, by her promise, set her intention of retirement at a distance, began imperceptibly to return to 30 common cares and common pleasures. She rejoiced without

her own consent at the suspension of her sorrows, and sometimes caught herself with indignation in the act of turning
away her mind from the remembrance of her, whom yet she
resolved never to forget.

She then appointed a certain hour of the day for meditation on the merits and fondness of Pekuah, and for some
weeks retired constantly at the time fixed, and returned with
her eyes swollen and her countenance clouded. By degrees
she grew less scrupulous, and suffered any important and
pressing avocation to delay the tribute of daily tears. She
then yielded to less occasions; sometimes forgot what she
was indeed afraid to remember, and at last wholly released
herself from the duty of periodical affliction.

Her real love of Pekuah was yet not diminished. A
thousand occurrences brought her back to memory, and a
thousand wants, which nothing but the confidence of friendship can supply, made her frequently regretted. She, therefore, solicited Imlac never to desist from inquiry, and to leave
no art of intelligence untried, that at least she might have
the comfort of knowing that she did not suffer by negligence
or sluggishness. 'Yet what,' said she, 'is to be expected
from our pursuit of happiness, when we find the state of life
to be such, that happiness itself is the cause of misery?
Why should we endeavour to attain that of which the possession cannot be secured? I shall henceforward fear to
yield my heart to excellence however bright, or to fondness
however tender, lest I should lose again what I have lost in
Pekuah.'

CHAPTER XXXVII.

THE PRINCESS HEARS NEWS OF PEKUAH.

In seven months, one of the messengers, who had been
sent away upon the day when the promise was drawn from

the princess, returned, after many unsuccessful rambles, from the borders of Nubia, with an account that Pekuah was in the hands of an Arab chief, who possessed a castle or fortress on the extremity of Egypt. The Arab, whose revenue was plunder, was willing to restore her, with her two attendants, for two hundred ounces of gold.

The price was no subject of debate. The princess was in ecstasies, when she heard that her favourite was alive, and might so cheaply be ransomed. She could not think of delaying for a moment Pekuah's happiness or her own, but entreated her brother to send back the messenger with the sum required. Imlac being consulted, was not very confident of the veracity of the relator, and was still more doubtful of the Arab's faith, who might, if he were too liberally trusted, detain at once the money and the captives. He thought it dangerous to put themselves in the power of the Arab, by going into his district, and could not expect that the rover would so much expose himself as to come into the lower country, where he might be seized by the forces of the Bassa.

It is difficult to negotiate where neither will trust. But Imlac, after some deliberation, directed the messenger to propose, that Pekuah should be conducted by ten horsemen to the monastery of St. Antony, which is situated in the deserts of Upper Egypt, where she should be met by the same number, and her ransom should be paid.

That no time might be lost, as they expected that the proposal would not be refused, they immediately began their journey to the monastery; and when they arrived, Imlac went forward with the former messenger to the Arab's fortress. Rasselas was desirous to go with them, but neither his sister nor Imlac would consent. The Arab, according to the custom of his nation, observed the laws of hospitality with great exactness to those who put themselves into his power, and, in a few days, brought Pekuah with her maids, by easy journeys, to the place appointed, where, receiving the stipulated price, he restored her with great respect to liberty and her friends, and undertook to conduct them back towards Cairo, beyond all danger of robbery or violence.

The princess and her favourite embraced each other with transport too violent to be expressed, and went out together to pour the tears of tenderness in secret, and exchange professions of kindness and gratitude. After a few hours they returned into the refectory of the convent, where, in the presence of the prior and his brethren, the prince required of Pekuah the history of her adventures.

CHAPTER XXXVIII.

THE ADVENTURES OF THE LADY PEKUAH.

' At what time and in what manner I was forced away,' said Pekuah, ' your servants have told you. The suddenness of the event struck me with surprise, and I was at first rather stupified, than agitated with any passion of either fear or sorrow. My confusion was increased by the speed and tumult of our flight, while we were followed by the Turks, who, as it seemed, soon despaired to overtake us, or were afraid of those whom they made a show of menacing.

' When the Arabs saw themselves out of danger, they slackened their course; and as I was less harassed by external violence, I began to feel more uneasiness in my mind. After some time, we stopped near a spring shaded with trees in a pleasant meadow, where we were set upon the ground, and offered such refreshments as our masters were partaking. I was suffered to sit with my maids apart from the rest, and none attempted to comfort or insult us. Here I first began to feel the full weight of my misery. The girls sat weeping in silence, and from time to time looked on me for succour. I knew not to what condition we were doomed, nor could conjecture where would be the place of our captivity, or whence to draw any hope of deliverance. I was in the hands of robbers and savages, and had no reason to suppose that their pity was more than their justice, or that they would forbear the gratification of any ardour of desire, or caprice of cruelty. I, however, kissed my maids, and endeavoured to pacify them by remarking that we were yet treated with decency, and that, since we were now carried beyond pursuit, there was no danger of violence to our lives.

'When we were to be set again on horseback, my maids clung round me, and refused to be parted; but I commanded them not to irritate those who had us in their power. We travelled the remaining part of the day through an unfrequented and pathless country, and came by moonlight to the side of a hill, where the rest of the troop were stationed. Their tents were pitched and their fires kindled, and our chief was welcomed as a man much beloved by his dependants.

'We were received into a large tent, where we found women who had attended their husbands in the expedition. They set before us the supper which they had provided, and I ate it rather to encourage my maids, than to comply with any appetite of my own. When the meat was taken away, they spread the carpets for repose. I was weary, and hoped to find in sleep that remission of distress which nature seldom denies. Ordering myself therefore to be undressed, I observed that the women looked very earnestly upon me, not expecting, I suppose, to see me so submissively attended. When my upper vest was taken off, they were apparently struck with the splendour of my clothes, and one of them timorously laid her hand upon the embroidery. She then went out, and in a short time came back with another woman, who seemed to be of higher rank and greater authority. She did, at her entrance, the usual act of reverence, and taking me by the hand, placed me in a smaller tent, spread with finer carpets, where I spent the night quietly with my maids.

'In the morning, as I was sitting on the grass, the chief of the troop came towards me. I rose up to receive him, and he bowed with great respect. "Illustrious lady," said 10 he, "my fortune is better than I had presumed to hope: I am told by my women that I have a princess in my camp." "Sir," answered I, "your women have deceived themselves and you; I am not a princess, but an unhappy stranger, who intended soon to have left this country, in which I am now to be imprisoned for ever." "Whoever or whencesoever you are," returned the Arab, "your dress, and that of your servants, show your rank to be high and your wealth to be great. Why should you, who can so easily procure your ransom, think yourself in danger of perpetual captivity? 20 The purpose of my incursions is to increase my riches, or, more properly, to gather tribute. The sons of Ishmael are the natural and hereditary lords of this part of the continent, which is usurped by late invaders and low-born tyrants, from whom we are compelled to take by the sword what is denied to justice. The violence of war admits no distinction; the lance that is lifted at guilt and power, will sometimes fall on innocence and gentleness."

'"How little," said I, "did I expect that yesterday it should have fallen upon me!"

30 '"Misfortunes," answered the Arab, "should always be expected. If the eye of hostility could learn reverence or pity, excellence like yours had been exempt from injury. But the angels of affliction spread their toils alike for the virtuous and the wicked, for the mighty and the mean. Do

not be disconsolate: I am not one of the lawless and cruel rovers of the desert; I know the rules of civil life; I will fix your ransom, give a passport to your messenger, and perform my stipulation with nice punctuality."

'You will easily believe that I was pleased with his courtesy: and finding that his predominant passion was desire of money, I began now to think my danger less, for I knew that no sum would be thought too great for the release of Pekuah. I told him that he should have no reason to charge me with ingratitude, if I was used with kindness, and that any ransom which could be expected for a maid of common rank would be paid; but that he must not persist to rate me as a princess. He said he would consider what he should demand, and then smiling, bowed and retired.

'Soon after, the women came about me, each contending to be more officious than the other, and my maids themselves were served with reverence. We travelled onward by short journeys. On the fourth day, the chief told me that my ransom must be two hundred ounces of gold; which I not only promised him, but told him, that I would add fifty more, if I and my maids were honourably treated.

'I never knew the power of gold before. From that time I was the leader of the troop. The march of every day was longer or shorter as I commanded, and the tents were pitched where I chose to rest. We now had camels and other conveniences for travel; my own women were always at my side; and I amused myself with observing the manners of the vagrant nations, and with viewing remains of ancient edifices, with which these deserted countries appear to have been, in some distant age, lavishly embellished.

'The chief of the band was a man far from illiterate: he was able to travel by the stars or the compass, and had marked, in his erratic expeditions, such places as are most worthy the notice of a passenger. He observed to me, that

buildings are always best preserved in places little frequented
and difficult of access: for, when once a country declines
from its primitive splendour, the more inhabitants are left,
the quicker ruin will be made. Walls supply stones more
easily than quarries, and palaces and temples will be
demolished, to make stables of granite and cottages of
porphyry.

CHAPTER XXXIX.

THE ADVENTURES OF PEKUAH CONTINUED.

'WE wandered about in this manner for some weeks,
whether, as our chief pretended, for my gratification, or, as
I rather suspected, for some convenience of his own. I
endeavoured to appear contented, where sullenness and
resentment would have been of no use, and that endeavour
conduced much to the calmness of my mind; but my heart
was always with Nekayah, and the troubles of the night
much overbalanced the amusements of the day. My women,
who threw all their cares upon their mistress, set their minds
at ease from the time when they saw me treated with respect,
and gave themselves up to the incidental alleviations of our
fatigue without solicitude or sorrow. I was pleased with
their pleasure, and animated with their confidence. My
condition had lost much of its terror, since I found that the
Arab ranged the country merely to get riches. Avarice is an
uniform and tractable vice: other intellectual distempers are
different in different constitutions of mind; that which
soothes the pride of one will offend the pride of another;
but to the favour of the covetous there is a ready way; bring
money, and nothing is denied.

'At last we came to the dwelling of our chief, a strong
and spacious house built with stone in an island of the Nile,

which lies, as I was told, under the tropic. "Lady," said the Arab, "you shall rest after your journey a few weeks in this place, where you are to consider yourself as sovereign. My occupation is war: I have therefore chosen this obscure residence, from which I can issue unexpected, and to which I can retire unpursued. You may now repose in security; here are few pleasures, but here is no danger." He then led me into the inner apartments, and seating me on the richest couch, bowed to the ground. His women, who considered me as a rival, looked on me with malignity; but being soon informed that I was a great lady detained only for my ransom, they began to vie with each other in obsequiousness and reverence.

'Being again comforted with new assurances of speedy liberty, I was for some days diverted from impatience by the novelty of the place. The turrets overlooked the country to a great distance, and afforded a view of many windings of the stream. In the day I wandered from one place to another, as the course of the sun varied the splendour of the prospect, and saw many things which I had never seen before. The crocodiles and river-horses are common in this unpeopled region, and I often looked upon them with terror, though I knew that they could not hurt me. For some time I expected to see mermaids and tritons, which, as Imlac has told me, the European travellers have stationed in the Nile; but no such beings ever appeared, and the Arab, when I inquired after them, laughed at my credulity.

'At night the Arab always attended me to a tower set apart for celestial observations, where he endeavoured to teach me the names and courses of the stars. I had no great inclination to this study, but an appearance of attention was necessary to please my instructor, who valued himself for his skill; and, in a little while, I found some employment requisite to beguile the tediousness of time, which was to be passed always amidst the same objects. I was weary of looking in the morning on things from which I had turned away weary in the evening; I therefore was at last willing to observe the stars rather than do nothing, but could not always compose my thoughts, and was very often thinking on Nekayah, when others imagined me contemplating the sky. Soon after, the Arab went upon another expedition, and then my only pleasure was to talk with my maids about the accident by which we were carried away, and the happiness that we should all enjoy at the end of our captivity.'

'There were women in your Arab's fortress,' said the princess: 'why did you not make them your companions, enjoy their conversation, and partake their diversions? In a place where they found business or amusement, why should you alone sit corroded with idle melancholy? or why could not you bear for a few months that condition to which they were condemned for life?'

'The diversions of the women,' answered Pekuah, 'were only childish play, by which the mind accustomed to stronger operations could not be kept busy. I could do all which they delighted in doing, by powers merely sensitive, while my intellectual faculties were flown to Cairo. They ran from room to room, as a bird hops from wire to wire in his cage. They danced for the sake of motion, as lambs frisk in a meadow. One sometimes pretended to be hurt, that the rest might be alarmed; or hid herself, that another might seek her. Part of their time passed in watching the progress of light bodies that floated on the river, and part in marking the various forms into which clouds broke in the sky.

'Their business was only needlework, in which I and my maids sometimes helped them; but you know that the mind will easily straggle from the fingers, nor will you suspect that captivity and absence from Nekayah could receive solace from silken flowers.

'Nor was much satisfaction to be hoped from their conversation: for of what could they be expected to talk? They had seen nothing, for they had lived from early youth in that narrow spot; of what they had not seen they could have no knowledge, for they could not read. They had no ideas but of the few things that were within their view, and had hardly names for any thing but their clothes and their food. As I bore a superior character, I was often called to terminate their quarrels, which I decided as equitably as I could. If it could have amused me to hear the complaints of each against the rest, I might have been often detained by long stories; but the motives of their animosity were so small, that I could not listen without intercepting the tale.'

'How,' said Rasselas, 'can the Arab, whom you represented as a man of more than common accomplishments, take any pleasure in his seraglio, when it is filled only with women like these? Are they exquisitely beautiful?'

'They do not,' said Pekuah, 'want that unaffecting and ignoble beauty which may subsist without sprightliness or sublimity, without energy of thought or dignity of virtue. But to a man like the Arab such beauty was only a flower casually plucked and carelessly thrown away. Whatever pleasures he might find among them, they were not those of friendship or society. When they were playing about him, he looked on them with inattentive superiority; when they vied for his regard, he sometimes turned away disgusted. As they had no knowledge, their talk could take nothing from the tediousness of life; as they had no choice, their fondness, or appearance of fondness, excited in him neither pride nor gratitude; he was not exalted in his own esteem by the smiles of a woman who saw no other man, nor was much obliged by that regard, of which he could never know the sincerity, and which he might often perceive to be exerted, not so much to delight him as to pain a rival

That which he gave and they received as love, was only a careless distribution of superfluous time, such love as man can bestow upon that which he despises, such as has neither hope, nor fear, neither joy nor sorrow.'

'You have reason, lady, to think yourself happy,' said Imlac, 'that you have been thus easily dismissed. How could a mind, hungry for knowledge, be willing, in an intellectual famine, to lose such a banquet as Pekuah's conversation?'

'I am inclined to believe,' answered Pekuah, 'that he was for some time in suspense; for, notwithstanding his promise, whenever I proposed to despatch a messenger to Cairo, he found some excuse for delay. While I was detained in his house, he made many incursions into the neighbouring countries; and, perhaps, he would have refused to discharge me, had his plunder been equal to his wishes. He returned always courteous, related his adventures, delighted to hear my observations, and endeavoured to advance my acquaintance with the stars. When I importuned him to send away my letters, he soothed me with professions of honour and sincerity; and, when I could be no longer decently denied, put his troop again in motion, and left me to govern in his absence. I was much afflicted by this studied procrastination, and was sometimes afraid that I should be forgotten; that you would leave Cairo, and I must end my days in an island of the Nile.

'I grew at last hopeless and dejected and cared so little to entertain him, that he for a while more frequently talked with my maids. That he should fall in love with them or with me, might have been equally fatal, and I was not much pleased with the growing friendship. My anxiety was not long; for, as I recovered some degree of cheerfulness, he returned to me, and I could not forbear to despise my former uneasiness.

'He still delayed to send for my ransom, and would, perhaps, never have determined, had not your agent found his way to him. The gold, which he would not fetch, he could not reject when it was offered. He hastened to prepare for our journey hither, like a man delivered from the pain of an intestine conflict. I took leave of my companions in the house, who dismissed me with cold indifference.'

Nekayah having heard her favourite's relation, rose and embraced her, and Rasselas gave her an hundred ounces of gold, which she presented to the Arab for the fifty that were promised.

CHAPTER XL.

THE HISTORY OF A MAN OF LEARNING.

THEY returned to Cairo, and were so well pleased at finding themselves together, that none of them went much abroad. The prince began to love learning, and one day declared to Imlac, that he intended to devote himself to science, and pass the rest of his days in literary solitude.

'Before you make your final choice,' answered Imlac, 'you ought to examine its hazards, and converse with some of those who are grown old in the company of themselves. I have just left the observatory of one of the most learned astronomers in the world, who has spent forty years in unwearied attention to the motions and appearances of the celestial bodies, and has drawn out his soul in endless calculations. He admits a few friends once a month, to hear his deductions and enjoy his discoveries. I was introduced as a man of knowledge worthy of his notice. Men of various ideas and fluent conversation, are commonly welcome to those whose thoughts have been long fixed upon a single point, and who find the images of other things stealing away. I delighted him with my remarks; he smiled at the narrative of my travels, and was glad to forget the constellations, and descend for a moment into the lower world.

'On the next day of vacation I renewed my visit, and was so fortunate as to please him again. He relaxed from that time the severity of his rule, and permitted me to enter at my own choice. I found him always busy, and always glad to be relieved. As each knew much which the other was desirous of learning, we exchanged our notions with great delight. I perceived that I had every day more of his confidence, and always found new cause of admiration in the profundity of his mind. His comprehension is vast, his memory capacious and retentive, his discourse is methodical, and his expression clear.

'His integrity and benevolence are equal to his learning. His deepest researches and most favourite studies are willingly interrupted for any opportunity of doing good by his counsel or his riches. To his closest retreat, at his most busy moments, all are admitted that want his assistance: "For though I exclude idleness and pleasure, I will never," says he, "bar my doors against charity. To man is permitted the contemplation of the skies, but the practice of virtue is commanded."'

'Surely,' said the princess, 'this man is happy.'

'I visited him,' said Imlac, 'with more and more frequency, and was every time more enamoured of his conversation; he was sublime without haughtiness, courteous without formality, and communicative without ostentation. I was at first, great princess, of your opinion, thought him the happiest of mankind, and often congratulated him on the blessing that he enjoyed. He seemed to hear nothing with indifference but the praises of his condition, to which he always returned a general answer, and diverted the conversation to some other topic.

'Amidst this willingness to be pleased and labour to please, I had quickly reason to imagine that some painful sentiment pressed upon his mind. He often looked up earnestly towards the sun, and let his voice fall in the midst of his discourse. He would sometimes, when we were alone, gaze upon me in silence, with the air of a man who longed to speak what he was yet resolved to suppress. He would often send for me with vehement injunctions of haste, though, when I came to him, he had nothing extraordinary to say; and sometimes, when I was leaving him, would call me back, pause a few moments, and then dismiss me.

CHAPTER XLI.

THE ASTRONOMER DISCOVERS THE CAUSE OF HIS UNEASINESS.

'At last the time came when the secret burst his reserve. We were sitting together last night in the turret of his house, watching the emersion of a satellite of Jupiter. A sudden tempest clouded the sky, and disappointed our observation. We sat awhile silent in the dark, and then he addressed himself to me in these words: "Imlac, I have long considered thy friendship as the greatest blessing of my life. Integrity without knowledge is weak and useless, and knowledge without integrity is dangerous and dreadful. I have found in thee all the qualities requisite for trust,— benevolence, experience, and fortitude. I have long discharged an office which I must soon quit at the call of nature, and shall rejoice in the hour of imbecility and pain to devolve it upon thee."

'I thought myself honoured by this testimony, and pro-

tested, that whatever could conduce to his happiness would
add likewise to mine.

' " Hear, Imlac, what thou wilt not without difficulty credit.
I have possessed for five years the regulation of the weather,
and the distribution of the seasons; the sun has listened to
my dictates, and passed from tropic to tropic by my direction; the clouds, at my call, have poured their waters, and
the Nile has overflowed at my command; I have restrained
the rage of the dog-star, and mitigated the fervours of the
crab.   The winds alone, of all the elemental powers, have
hitherto refused my authority, and multitudes have perished
by equinoctial tempests, which I found myself unable to
prohibit or restrain.   I have administered this great office
with exact justice, and made to the different nations of the
earth an impartial dividend of rain and sunshine.   What
must have been the misery of half the globe, if I had limited
the clouds to particular regions, or confined the sun to either
side of the equator?"

CHAPTER XLII.

THE OPINION OF THE ASTRONOMER IS EXPLAINED AND
JUSTIFIED.

' I suppose he discovered in me, through the obscurity of
the room, some tokens of amazement and doubt, for, after a
short pause, he proceeded thus:

' " Not to be easily credited will neither surprise nor
offend me; for I am, probably, the first of human beings
to whom this trust has been imparted.   Nor do I know
whether to deem this distinction a reward or punishment;
since I have possessed it, I have been far less happy than
before, and nothing but the consciousness of good intention

could have enabled me to support the weariness of unremitted vigilance."

' " How long, sir," said I, " has this great office been in your hands?"

' " About ten years ago," said he, " my daily observations of the changes of the sky led me to consider, whether, if I had the power of the seasons, I could confer greater plenty upon the inhabitants of the earth. This contemplation fastened on my mind, and I sat days and nights in imaginary dominion, pouring upon this country and that the showers of fertility, and seconding every fall of rain with a due proportion of sunshine. I had yet only the will to do good, and did not imagine that I should ever have the power.

' " One day, as I was looking on the fields withering with heat, I felt in my mind a sudden wish that I could send rain on the southern mountains, and raise the Nile to an inundation. In the hurry of my imagination I commanded rain to fall; and by comparing the time of my command with that of the inundation, I found that the clouds had listened to my lips."

' " Might not some other cause," said I, " produce this concurrence? the Nile does not always rise on the same day."

' " Do not believe," said he with impatience, " that such objections could escape me: I reasoned long against my own conviction, and laboured against truth with the utmost obstinacy. I sometimes suspected myself of madness, and should not have dared to impart this secret but to a man like you, capable of distinguishing the wonderful from the impossible, and the incredible from the false."

' " Why, sir," said I, " do you call that incredible, which you know, or think you know, to be true?"

' " Because," said he, " I cannot prove it by any external

evidence; and I know too well the laws of demonstration to think that my conviction ought to influence another, who cannot like me be conscious of its force. I therefore shall not attempt to gain credit by disputation. It is sufficient that I feel this power, that I have long possessed, and every day exerted it. But the life of man is short, the infirmities of age increase upon me, and the time will soon come, when the regulator of the year must mingle with the dust. The care of appointing a successor has long disturbed me; the night and the day have been spent in comparisons of all the characters which have come to my knowledge, and I have yet found none so worthy as thyself."

CHAPTER XLIII.

THE ASTRONOMER LEAVES IMLAC HIS DIRECTIONS.

' "Hear, therefore, what I shall impart, with attention such as the welfare of a world requires. If the task of a king be considered as difficult, who has the care only of a few millions, to whom he cannot do much good or harm, what must be the anxiety of him on whom depends the action of the elements, and the great gifts of light and heat! Hear me therefore with attention.

' "I have diligently considered the position of the earth and sun, and formed innumerable schemes in which I changed their situation. I have sometimes turned aside the axis of the earth, and sometimes varied the ecliptic of the sun; but I have found it impossible to make a disposition by which the world may be advantaged; what one region gains, another loses, by an imaginable alteration, even without considering the distant parts of the solar system with which we are unacquainted. Do not, therefore,

in thy administration of the year, indulge thy pride by inno-
vation ; do not please thyself with thinking that thou canst
make thyself renowned to all future ages by disordering the
seasons. The memory of mischief is no desirable fame.
Much less will it become thee to let kindness or interest
prevail. Never rob other countries of rain to pour it on
thine own. For us the Nile is sufficient."

'I promised, that when I possessed the power, I would
use it with inflexible integrity ; and he dismissed me, pressing
my hand. "My heart," said he, "will be now at rest, and
my benevolence will no more destroy my quiet ; I have
found a man of wisdom and virtue, to whom I can cheerfully
bequeath the inheritance of the sun."'

The prince heard this narration with very serious regard ;
but the princess smiled, and Pekuah convulsed herself with
laughter. 'Ladies,' said Imlac, 'to mock the heaviest of
human affliction is neither charitable nor wise. Few can
attain this man's knowledge, and few practise his virtues ;
but all may suffer his calamity. Of the uncertainties of our
present state, the most dreadful and alarming is the uncertain
continuance of reason.'

The princess was recollected, and the favourite was
abashed. Rasselas, more deeply affected, inquired of Imlac,
whether he thought such maladies of the mind frequent, and
how they were contracted.

CHAPTER XLIV.

THE DANGEROUS PREVALENCE OF IMAGINATION.

'DISORDERS of intellect,' answered Imlac, 'happen much
more often than superficial observers will easily believe.
Perhaps, if we speak with rigorous exactness, no human

mind is in its right state. There is no man whose imagination does not sometimes predominate over his reason,
who can regulate his attention wholly by his will, and whose
ideas will come and go at his command. No man will be
found in whose mind airy notions do not sometimes tyran-
nise, and force him to hope or fear beyond the limits of sober
probability. All power of fancy over reason is a degree of
insanity; but while this power is such as we can control and
repress, it is not visible to others, nor considered as any
depravation of the mental faculties : it is not pronounced
madness, but when it becomes ungovernable and apparently
influences speech or action.

'To indulge the power of fiction, and send imagination
out upon the wing, is often the sport of those who delight
too much in silent speculation. When we are alone we are
not always busy; the labour of excogitation is too violent to
last long; the ardour of inquiry will sometimes give way to
idleness or satiety. He who has nothing external that can
divert him, must find pleasure in his own thoughts, and
must conceive himself what he is not; for who is pleased
with what he is? He then expatiates in boundless futurity,
and culls from all imaginable conditions that which for the
present moment he should most desire, amuses his desires
with impossible enjoyments, and confers upon his pride
unattainable dominion. The mind dances from scene to
scene, unites all pleasures in all combinations, and riots in
delights, which nature and fortune, with all their bounty,
cannot bestow.

'In time some particular train of ideas fixes the attention;
all other intellectual gratifications are rejected; the mind, in
weariness or leisure, recurs constantly to the favourite conception, and feasts on the luscious falsehood whenever she is
offended with the bitterness of truth. By degrees the reign
of fancy is confirmed; she grows first imperious, and in time

despotic. Then fictions begin to operate as realities, false opinions fasten upon the mind, and life passes in dreams of rapture or of anguish.

'This, sir, is one of the dangers of solitude, which the hermit has confessed not always to promote goodness, and the astronomer's misery has proved to be not always propitious to wisdom.'

'I will no more,' said the favourite, 'imagine myself the queen of Abyssinia. I have often spent the hours which the princess gave to my own disposal, in adjusting cere- monies and regulating the court; I have repressed the pride of the powerful and granted the petitions of the poor; I have built new palaces in more happy situations, planted groves upon the tops of mountains, and have exulted in the beneficence of royalty, till, when the princess entered, I had almost forgotten to bow down before her.'

'And I,' said the princess, ' will not allow myself any more to play the shepherdess in my waking dreams. I have often soothed my thoughts with the quiet and innocence of pastoral employments, till I have in my chamber heard the winds whistle, and the sheep bleat; sometimes freed the lamb entangled in the thicket, and sometimes with my crook encountered the wolf. I have a dress like that of the village maids, which I put on to help my imagination, and a pipe on which I play softly, and suppose myself followed by my flocks.'

'I will confess,' said the prince, 'an indulgence of fantastic delight more dangerous than yours. I have frequently endeavoured to image the possibility of a perfect government, by which all wrong should be restrained, all vice reformed, and all the subjects preserved in tranquillity and innocence. This thought produced innumerable schemes of reformation, and dictated many useful regulations and salutary edicts. This has been the sport and sometimes the labour, of my

solitude; and I start when I think with how little anguish I
once supposed the death of my father and my brothers.'

'Such,' says Imlac, 'are the effects of visionary schemes.
When we first form them, we know them to be absurd, but
familiarise them by degrees, and in time lose sight of their
folly.'

CHAPTER XLV.

THEY DISCOURSE WITH AN OLD MAN.

THE evening was now far past, and they rose to return
home. As they walked along the bank of the Nile, delighted
with the beams of the moon quivering on the water, they saw
at a small distance an old man, whom the prince had often
neard in the assembly of the sages. 'Yonder,' said he, 'is
one whose years have calmed his passions, but not clouded
his reason; let us close the disquisitions of the night, by
inquiring what are his sentiments of his own state, that we
may know whether youth alone is to struggle with vexation,
and whether any better hope remains for the latter part of
life.'

Here the sage approached and saluted them. They
invited him to join their walk, and prattled awhile, as acquaintance that had unexpectedly met one another. The
old man was cheerful and talkative, and the way seemed
short in his company. He was pleased to find himself not
disregarded, accompanied them to their house, and, at the
prince's request, entered with them. They placed him in
the seat of honour, and set wine and conserves before him.

'Sir,' said the princess, 'an evening walk must give to
a man of learning, like you, pleasures which ignorance and
youth can hardly conceive. You know the qualities and the

causes of all that you behold, the laws by which the river flows, the periods in which the planets perform their revolutions. Every thing must supply you with contemplation, and renew the consciousness of your own dignity.'

' Lady,' answered he, ' let the gay and the vigorous expect pleasure in their excursions; it is enough that age can obtain ease. To me the world has lost its novelty: I look round, and see what I remember to have seen in happier days. I rest against a tree, and consider, that in the same shade I once disputed upon the annual overflow of the Nile with a friend who is now silent in the grave. I cast my eyes upwards, fix them on the changing moon, and think with pain on the vicissitudes of life. I have ceased to take much delight in physical truth; for what have I to do with those things which I am soon to leave !'

' You may at least recreate yourself,' said Imlac, ' with the recollection of an honourable and useful life, and enjoy the praise which all agree to give you.'

' Praise,' said the sage with a sigh, ' is to an old man an empty sound. I have neither mother to be delighted with the reputation of her son, nor wife to partake the honours of her husband. I have outlived my friends and my rivals. Nothing is now of much importance; for I cannot extend my interest beyond myself. Youth is delighted with applause, because it is considered as the earnest of some future good, and because the prospect of life is far extended; but to me, who am now declining to decrepitude, there is little to be feared from the malevolence of men, and yet less to be hoped from their affection or esteem. Something they may yet take away, but they can give me nothing. Riches would now be useless, and high employment would be pain. My retrospect of life recalls to my view many opportunities of good neglected, much time squandered upon trifles, and more lost in idleness and vacancy. I leave many great designs unattempted, and many great attempts unfinished. My mind is burdened with no heavy crime, and therefore I compose myself to tranquillity; endeavour to abstract my thoughts from hopes and cares, which, though reason knows them to be vain, still try to keep their old possession of the heart; expect, with serene humility, that hour which nature cannot long delay; and hope to possess, in a better state, that happiness which here I could not find, and that virtue which here I have not attained.'

10 He rose and went away, leaving his audience not much elated with the hope of long life. The prince consoled himself with remarking, that it was not reasonable to be disappointed by this account, for age had never been considered as the season of felicity, and if it was possible to be easy in decline and weakness, it was likely that the days of vigour and alacrity might be happy: that the noon of life might be bright, if the evening could be calm.

The princess suspected that age was querulous and malignant, and delighted to repress the expectations of those 20 who had newly entered the world. She had seen the possessors of estates look with envy on their heirs, and known many who enjoyed pleasure no longer than they can confine it to themselves.

Pekuah conjectured that the man was older than he appeared, and was willing to impute his complaints to delirious dejection; or else supposed that he had been unfortunate, and was therefore discontented; 'For nothing,' said she, 'is more common, than to call our own condition the condition of life.'

30 Imlac, who had no desire to see them depressed, smiled at the comforts which they could so readily procure to themselves, and remembered, that at the same age he was equally confident of unmingled prosperity, and equally fertile of consolatory expedients. He forbore to force on them unwel-

come knowledge, which time itself would too soon impress. The princess and her lady retired; the madness of the astronomer hung upon their minds, and they desired Imlac to enter upon his office, and delay next morning the rising of the sun.

CHAPTER XLVI.

THE PRINCESS AND PEKUAH VISIT THE ASTRONOMER.

THE princess and Pekuah having talked in private of Imlac's astronomer, thought his character at once so amiable and so strange, that they could not be satisfied without a nearer knowledge; and Imlac was requested to find the means of bringing them together.

This was somewhat difficult: the philosopher had never received any visits from women, though he lived in a city that had in it many Europeans, who followed the manners of their own countries, and many from other parts of the world, that lived there with European liberty. The ladies would not be refused, and several schemes were proposed for the accomplishment of their design. It was proposed to introduce them as strangers in distress, to whom the sage was always accessible; but, after some deliberation, it appeared that by this artifice no acquaintance could be formed, for their conversation would be short, and they could not decently importune him often. 'This,' said Rasselas, 'is true; but I have yet a stronger objection against the misrepresentation of your state. I have always considered it as treason against the great republic of human nature, to make any man's virtues the means of deceiving him, whether on great or little occasions. All imposture weakens confidence, and chills benevolence. When the sage finds that you are not what you seemed, he will feel the resentment natural to a man who, conscious of great abilities, discovers that he has been tricked by understandings meaner than his own, and, perhaps, the distrust which he can never afterwards wholly lay aside, may stop the voice of counsel and close the hand of charity; and where will you find the power of restoring his benefactions to mankind, or his peace to himself?'

To this no reply was attempted, and Imlac began to hope that their curiosity would subside; but, next day, Pekuah told him, she had now found an honest pretence for a visit to the astronomer, for she would solicit permission to continue under him the studies in which she had been initiated by the Arab, and the princess might go with her either as a fellow-student, or because a woman could not decently come alone. 'I am afraid,' said Imlac, 'that he will be soon weary of your company; men advanced far in knowledge do not love to repeat the elements of their art, and I am not certain that even of the elements, as he will deliver them, connected with inferences and mingled with reflexions, you are a very capable auditress.'—'That,' said Pekuah, 'must be my care; I ask of you only to take me thither. My knowledge is, perhaps, more than you imagine it; and, by concurring always with his opinions, I shall make him think it greater than it is.'

The astronomer, in pursuance of this resolution, was told that a foreign lady, travelling in search of knowledge, had heard of his reputation, and was desirous to become his scholar. The uncommonness of the proposal raised at once his surprise and curiosity; and when, after a short deliberation, he consented to admit her, he could not stay without impatience till the next day.

The ladies dressed themselves magnificently, and were attended by Imlac to the astronomer, who was pleased to see himself approached with respect by persons of so splendid an appearance. In the exchange of the first civilities he was timorous and bashful; but when the talk became regular, he re-collected his powers, and justified the character which Imlac had given. Inquiring of Pekuah what could have turned her inclination towards astronomy, he received from her a history of her adventure at the Pyramid, and of the time passed in the Arab's island. She told her tale with ease and elegance, and her conversation took possession of his heart. The discourse was then turned to astronomy: Pekuah displayed what she knew: he looked upon her as a prodigy of genius, and entreated her not to desist from a ıc study which she had so happily begun.

They came again and again, and were every time more welcome than before. The sage endeavoured to amuse them, that they might prolong their visits, for he found his thoughts grow brighter in their company; the clouds of solicitude vanished by degrees, as he forced himself to entertain them, and he grieved when he was left at their departure to his old employment of regulating the seasons.

The princess and her favourite had now watched his lips for several months, and could not catch a single word from 20 which they could judge whether he continued, or not, in the opinion of his preternatural commission. They often contrived to bring him to an open declaration; but he easily eluded all their attacks, and, on which side soever they pressed him, escaped from them to some other topic.

As their familiarity increased, they invited him often to the house of Imlac, where they distinguished him by extraordinary respect. He began gradually to delight in sublunary pleasures. He came early, and departed late; laboured to recommend himself by assiduity and compliance; excited 3ᴏ their curiosity after new arts, that they might still want his assistance; and when they made any excursion of pleasure or inquiry, entreated to attend them.

By long experience of his integrity and wisdom, the prince

and his sister were convinced that he might be trusted without danger; and lest he should draw any false hopes from the civilities which he received, discovered to him their condition, with the motives of their journey, and required his opinion on the choice of life.

'Of the various conditions which the world spreads before you, which you shall prefer,' said the sage, 'I am not able to instruct you. I can only tell that I have chosen wrong. I have passed my time in study without experience; in the attainment of sciences which can, for the most part, be but remotely useful to mankind. I have purchased knowledge at the expense of all the common comforts of life; I have missed the endearing elegance of female friendship, and the happy commerce of domestic tenderness. If I have obtained any prerogatives above other students, they have been accompanied with fear, disquiet, and scrupulosity; but even of these prerogatives, whatever they were, I have, since my thoughts have been diversified by more intercourse with the world, begun to question the reality. When I have been for a few days lost in pleasing dissipation, I am always tempted to think that my inquiries have ended in error, and that I have suffered much and suffered it in vain.'

Imlac was delighted to find that the sage's understanding was breaking through its mists, and resolved to detain him from the planets till he should forget his task of ruling them, and reason should recover its original influence.

From this time the astronomer was received into familiar friendship, and partook of all their projects and pleasures; his respect kept him attentive, and the activity of Rasselas did not leave much time unengaged. Something was always to be done: the day was spent in making observations which furnished talk for the evening, and the evening was closed with a scheme for the morrow.

The sage confessed to Imlac, that since he had mingled in

the gay tumults of life, and divided his hours by a succession of amusements, he found the conviction of his authority over the skies fade gradually from his mind, and began to trust less to an opinion which he never could prove to others, and which he now found subject to variation, from causes in which reason had no part. 'If I am accidentally left alone for a few hours,' said he, ' my inveterate persuasion rushes upon my soul, and my thoughts are chained down by some irresistible violence; but they are soon disentangled by the prince's conversation, and instantaneously released at the entrance of Pekuah. I am like a man habitually afraid of spectres, who is set at ease by a lamp, and wonders at the dread which harassed him in the dark; yet, if his lamp be extinguished, feels again the terrors which he knows that when it is light he shall feel no more. But I am sometimes afraid lest I indulge my quiet by criminal negligence, and voluntarily forget the great charge with which I am intrusted. If I favour myself in a known error, or am determined by my own ease in a doubtful question of this importance, how dreadful is my crime!'

'No disease of the imagination,' answered Imlac, 'is so difficult of cure as that which is complicated with the dread of guilt; fancy and conscience then act interchangeably upon us, and so often shift their places, that the illusions of one are not distinguished from the dictates of the other. If fancy presents images not moral or religious, the mind drives them away when they give it pain; but when melancholic notions take the form of duty, they lay hold on the faculties without opposition, because we are afraid to exclude or banish them. For this reason the superstitious are often melancholy, and the melancholy almost always superstitious.

'But do not let the suggestions of timidity overpower your better reason: the danger of neglect can be but as the probability of the obligation, which, when you consider it with freedom, you find very little, and that little growing every day less. Open your heart to the influence of the light which from time to time breaks in upon you; when scruples importune you, which you in your lucid moments know to be vain, do not stand to parley, but fly to business, or to Pekuah, and keep this thought always prevalent, that you are only one atom of the mass of humanity, and have neither such virtue nor vice, as that you should be singled out for supernatural favours or afflictions.'

CHAPTER XLVII.

THE PRINCE ENTERS, AND BRINGS A NEW TOPIC.

'ALL this,' said the astronomer, 'I have often thought, but my reason has been so long subjugated by an uncontrollable and overwhelming idea, that it durst not confide in its own decisions. I now see how fatally I betrayed my quiet, by suffering chimeras to prey upon me in secret; but melancholy shrinks from communication, and I never found a man before to whom I could impart my troubles, though I had been certain of relief. I rejoice to find my own sentiments confirmed by yours, who are not easily deceived, and can have no motive or purpose to deceive. I hope that time and variety will dissipate the gloom that has so long surrounded me, and the latter part of my days will be spent in peace.'

'Your learning and virtue,' said Imlac, 'may justly give you hopes.'

Rasselas then entered with the princess and Pekuah, and inquired, whether they had contrived any new diversion for the next day. 'Such,' said Nekayah, 'is the state of life, that none are happy but by the anticipation of change:

the change itself is nothing; when we have made it, the next wish is to change again. The world is not yet exhausted; let me see something to-morrow which I never saw before.'

'Variety,' said Rasselas, 'is so necessary to content, that even the happy valley disgusted me by the recurrence of its luxuries; yet I could not forbear to reproach myself with impatience, when I saw the monks of St. Anthony support, without complaint, a life, not of uniform delight, but uniform hardship.'

'Those men,' answered Imlac, 'are less wretched in their silent convent, than the Abyssinian princes in their prison of pleasure. Whatever is done by the monks is incited by an adequate and reasonable motive. Their labour supplies them with necessaries; it therefore cannot be omitted, and is certainly rewarded. Their devotion prepares them for another state, and reminds them of its approach while it fits them for it. Their time is regularly distributed : one duty succeeds another, so that they are not left open to the distraction of unguided choice, nor lost in the shades of listless inactivity. There is a certain task to be performed at an appropriated hour; and their toils are cheerful, because they consider them as acts of piety by which they are always advancing towards endless felicity.'

'Do you think,' said Nekayah, 'that the monastic rule is a more holy and less imperfect state than any other? May not he equally hope for future happiness who converses openly with mankind, who succours the distressed by his charity, instructs the ignorant by his learning, and contributes by his industry to the general system of life; even though he should omit some of the mortifications which are practised in the cloister, and allow himself such harmless delights as his condition may place within his reach?'

'This,' said Imlac, 'is a question which has long divided

the wise, and perplexed the good. I am afraid to decide on either part. He that lives well in the world is better than he that lives well in a monastery. But, perhaps, every one is not able to stem the temptations of public life; and if he cannot conquer, he may properly retreat. Some have little power to do good, and have likewise little strength to resist evil. Many are weary of their conflicts with adversity, and are willing to eject those passions which have long busied them in vain. And many are dismissed by age and diseases from the more laborious duties of society. In monasteries, the weak and timorous may be happily sheltered, the weary may repose, and the penitent may meditate. Those retreats of prayer and contemplation have something so congenial to the mind of man, that, perhaps, there is scarcely one that does not purpose to close his life in pious abstraction, with a few associates serious as himself.'

'Such,' said Pekuah, 'has often been my wish, and I have heard the princess declare, that she would not willingly die in a crowd.'

'The liberty of using harmless pleasures,' proceeded Imlac, 'will not be disputed; but it is still to be examined what pleasures are harmless. The evil of any pleasure that Nekayah can image, is not in the act itself, but in its consequences. Pleasure, in itself harmless, may become mischievous, by endearing to us a state which we know to be transient and probatory, and withdrawing our thoughts from that of which every hour brings us nearer to the beginning, and of which no length of time will bring us to the end. Mortification is not virtuous in itself, nor has any other use, but that it disengages us from the allurements of sense. In the state of future perfection, to which we all aspire, there will be pleasure without danger, and security without restraint.'

The princess was silent; and Rasselas, turning to the

astronomer, asked him, whether he could not delay her retreat, by showing her something which she had not seen before.

'Your curiosity,' said the sage, 'has been so general, and your pursuit of knowledge so vigorous, that novelties are not now very easily to be found; but what you can no longer procure from the living may be given by the dead. Among the wonders of this country are the Catacombs, or the ancient repositories in which the bodies of the earliest generations were lodged, and where, by the virtue of the gums which 10 embalmed them, they yet remain without corruption.'

'I know not,' said Rasselas, 'what pleasure the sight of the Catacombs can afford; but, since nothing else offered, I am resolved to view them, and shall place this with many other things, which I have done because I would do something.'

They hired a guard of horsemen, and the next day visited the Catacombs. When they were about to descend into the sepulchral caves, 'Pekuah,' said the princess, 'we are now again invading the habitations of the dead; I know that you 20 will stay behind; let me find you safe when I return.'—'No; I will not be left,' answered Pekuah, 'I will go down between you and the prince.'

They then all descended, and roved with wonder through the labyrinth of subterraneous passages, where the bodies were laid in rows on either side.

CHAPTER XLVIII.

IMLAC DISCOURSES ON THE NATURE OF THE SOUL.

'WHAT reason,' said the prince, 'can be given, why the Egyptians should thus expensively preserve those carcases, 30 which some nations consume with fire, others lay to mingle with the earth, and all agree to remove from their sight as soon as decent rites can be performed?'

'The original of ancient customs,' said Imlac, 'is commonly unknown, for the practice often continues when the cause has ceased; and concerning superstitious ceremonies it is vain to conjecture, for what reason did not dictate reason cannot explain. I have long believed, that the practice of embalming arose only from tenderness to the remains of relations or friends, and to this opinion I am more inclined, because it seems impossible that this care should have been general: had all the dead been embalmed, their repositories must in time have been more spacious than the dwellings of the living. I suppose only the rich or honourable were secured from corruption, and the rest left to the course of nature.

'But it is commonly supposed, that the Egyptians believed the soul to live as long as the body continued undissolved, and therefore tried this method of eluding death.'

'Could the wise Egyptians,' said Nekayah, 'think so grossly of the soul? If the soul could once survive its separation, what could it afterwards receive or suffer from the body?'

'The Egyptians would doubtless think erroneously,' said the astronomer, 'in the darkness of heathenism, and the first dawn of philosophy. The nature of the soul is still disputed, amidst all our opportunities of clearer knowledge: some yet say that it may be material, who, nevertheless, believe it to be immortal.'

'Some,' answered Imlac, 'have indeed said that the soul is material, but I can scarcely believe that any man has thought it, who knew how to think; for all the conclusions of reason enforce the immateriality of mind, and all the notices of sense and investigations of science concur to prove the unconsciousness of matter.'

'It was never supposed that cogitation is inherent in matter, or that every particle is a thinking being. Yet, if any part of matter be devoid of thought, what part can we suppose to think? Matter can differ from matter only in form, density, bulk, motion, and direction of motion: to which of these, however varied or combined, can consciousness be annexed? To be round or square, to be solid or fluid, to be great or little, to be moved slowly or swiftly one way or another, are modes of material existence, all equally alien from the nature of cogitation. If matter be once without thought, it can only be made to think by some new modification; but all the modifications which it can admit are equally unconnected with cogitative powers.'

'But the materialists,' said the astronomer, 'urge that matter may have qualities with which we are unacquainted.'

'He who will determine,' returned Imlac, 'against that which he knows, because there may be something which he knows not,—he that can set hypothetical possibility against acknowledged certainty,—is not to be admitted among reasonable beings. All that we know of matter is, that matter is inert, senseless, and lifeless; and if this conviction cannot be opposed, but by referring us to something that we know not, we have all the evidence that human intellect can admit. If that which is known may be overruled by that which is unknown, no being, not omniscient, can arrive at certainty.'

'Yet let us not,' said the astronomer, 'too arrogantly limit the Creator's power.'

'It is no limitation of omnipotence,' replied the poet, 'to suppose that one thing is not consistent with another, that the same proposition cannot be at once true and false, that the same number cannot be even and odd, that cogitation cannot be conferred on that which is created incapable of cogitation.'

'I know not,' said Nekayah, 'any great use of this question. Does that immateriality, which, in my opinion, you have sufficiently proved, necessarily include eternal duration?'

'Of immateriality,' said Imlac, 'our ideas are negative, and therefore obscure. Immateriality seems to imply a natural power of perpetual duration as a consequence of exemption from all causes of decay; whatever perishes is destroyed by the solution of its contexture, and separation of its parts; nor can we conceive how that which has no parts, and therefore admits no solution, can be naturally corrupted or impaired.'

'I know not,' said Rasselas, 'how to conceive anything without extension; what is extended must have parts, and you allow that whatever has parts may be destroyed.'

'Consider your own conceptions,' replied Imlac, 'and the difficulty will be less. You will find substance without extension. An ideal form is no less real than material bulk; yet an ideal form has no extension. It is no less certain, when you think on a pyramid, that your mind possesses the idea of a pyramid, than that the pyramid itself is standing. What space does the idea of a pyramid occupy more than the idea of a grain of corn? or how can either idea suffer laceration? As is the effect, such is the cause: as thought, such is the power that thinks; a power impassive and indiscerptible.'

'But the Being,' said Nekayah, 'whom I fear to name, the Being which made the soul, can destroy it.'

'He surely can destroy it,' answered Imlac, 'since, however unperishable, it receives from a superior nature its power of duration. That it will not perish by any inherent cause of decay, or principle of corruption, may be shown by philosophy; but philosophy can tell no more. That it will not be annihilated by him that made it, we must humbly learn from higher authority.' The whole assembly stood awhile silent and collected. 'Let us return,' said Rasselas,

' from this scene of mortality. How gloomy would be these mansions of the dead to him who did not know that he should never die, that what now acts shall continue its agency, and what now thinks shall think on for ever. Those that lie here stretched before us, the wise and the powerful of ancient times, warn us to remember the shortness of our present state : they were, perhaps, snatched away while they were busy like us in the choice of life.'

' To me,' said the princess, ' the choice of life is become less important ; I hope hereafter to think only on the choice of eternity.'

They then hastened out of the caverns, and under the protection of their guard returned to Cairo.

CHAPTER XLIX.

THE CONCLUSION, IN WHICH NOTHING IS CONCLUDED.

IT was now the time of the inundation of the Nile: a few days after their visit to the catacombs, the river began to rise.

They were confined to their house. The whole region being under water gave them no invitation to any excursions, and, being well supplied with materials for talk, they diverted themselves with comparisons of the different forms of life which they had observed, and with various schemes of happiness which each of them had formed.

Pekuah was never so much charmed with any place as the convent of St. Anthony, where the Arab restored her to the princess, and wished only to fill it with pious maidens, and to be made prioress of the order ; she was weary of expectation and disgust, and would gladly be fixed in some unvariable state. 30

The princess thought, that of all sublunary things knowledge was the best: she desired first to learn all sciences, and then proposed to found a college of learned women, in which she would preside, that, by conversing with the old, and educating the young, she might divide her time between the acquisition and communication of wisdom, and raise up for the next age models of prudence, and patterns of piety.

The prince desired a little kingdom, in which he might administer justice in his own person, and see all the parts of government with his own eyes; but he could never fix the limits of his dominion, and was always adding to the number of his subjects.

Imlac and the astronomer were contented to be driven along the stream of life, without directing their course to any particular port.

Of these wishes that they had formed they well knew that none could be obtained. They deliberated awhile what was to be done, and resolved, when the inundation should cease, to return to Abyssinia.

THE END OF RASSELAS.

NOTES.

P. 37, l. 2. *Rasselas.* On p. 102 of Johnson's translation of Lobo's *Voyage to Abyssinia* mention is made of 'Rassela Christos, Lieutenant-General to Sultan Segued.' On p. 262 the first part of the word is thus explained : ' There is now a Generalissimo established under the title of *Ras* or *Chief.*' The title still exists. Ras Arya and Ras Aloula are mentioned in *Colonel Gordon in Central Africa.* The Rev. W. West, in his Introduction to *Rasselas*, p. xxxi, says : 'The word *Ras* signifies a *head*, and hence a prince, chief or captain. Sela Christos means either " Picture of Christ," or " For the sake of Christ." ' The Hebrew form of *Ras* is *Rosh*, which is found as a proper name in *Genesis* xlvi. 21, and *Ezekiel* (Revised Version) xxxviii. 2, 3, xxxix. 1.

l. 6. *Ye who—*

> 'Even such is time, that takes in trust
> Our youth, our joys, our all we have,
> And pays us but with earth and dust ;
> Who in the dark and silent grave,
> When we have wandered all our ways,
> Shuts up the story of our days ;
> But from this earth, this grave, this dust,
> My God shall raise me up, I trust.'

Found in Sir Walter Raleigh's Bible in the Gate-House at Westminster. *Poems of Raleigh*, ed. by J. Hannah, p. 54.

> 'When I consider life 'tis all a cheat,
> Yet fool'd with hope men favour the deceit ;
> Trust on, and think to-morrow will repay ;
> To-morrow's falser than the former day ;
> Lies worse, and while it says we shall be blest
> With some new joys cuts off what we possess.'

Dryden, Aurengzebe, Act iv. sc. 1.

'Condemned to Hope's delusive mine,
    As on we toil from day to day,
By sudden blast or slow decline
    Our social comforts drop away.'
    Johnson, *Lines to Levett*, Boswell's *Life of Johnson*, iv. 137.

l. 12. *mighty emperor.* Gibbon describes the power of 'the Negus, or supreme prince of Abyssinia,' in the sixth century (*Decline and Fall of the Roman Empire*, ed. 1862, v. 207). Writing of the latter half of the sixteenth century, he says : 'Their vessels, which had traded to Ceylon, scarcely presumed to navigate the rivers of Africa ; the ruins of Axume [the royal city] were deserted, the nation was scattered in villages, and the emperor, a pompous name, was content both in peace and war with the immoveable residence of a camp.'—*Ib.* vi. 64.

l. 13. *the Father of Waters.* 'The natives call the Nile Abavi, that is the Father of Waters.'—Lobo's *Abyssinia*, p. 97.

begins his course. The main body of the Nile, the White Nile, rises in the country round Lake Victoria Nyanza. The floods which give Egypt its fertility are caused by the Blue Nile and the Atbara, which both rise in Abyssinia. 'The lake-sources of Central Africa support the *life* of Egypt by supplying a stream throughout all seasons that has sufficient volume to support the exhaustion of evaporation and absorption ; but this stream, if unaided, could never overflow its banks, and Egypt, thus deprived of the annual inundation, would simply exist, and cultivation would be confined to the close vicinity of the river.' The rains which fall in Abyssinia from the middle of June until September turn the Blue Nile and the Atbara from streams almost dried up into mighty rivers. Pouring into the White Nile they cause the yearly inundation.—Baker's *Nile Tributaries of Abyssinia*, p. viii.

l. 14. *scatters* . . . . Gibbon, writing of the year A.D. 532, says : 'Abraham had been relieved by the well-known plenty of Egypt ; the same country, a small and populous tract, was still capable of exporting each year two hundred and sixty

thousand quarters of wheat for the use of Constantinople.'—
Decline and Fall, ed. 1862, v. 55. Egypt no longer ranks
among the chief grain-supplying countries.

l. 21. *The place.* According to Lobo (p. 204) it was not in
a valley, but 'on the barren summit of Ambaguexa in the
kingdom of Amhara that the princes of the blood-royal passed
their melancholy life, being guarded by officers who treated
them often with great rigour and severity.' 'These steep
rocks,' he adds, 'the Abyssins call *Amba.*' On p. 259 he says
that from among these princes the Emperor could choose his
successor. If he omitted to do so, the choice was made by the
grandees of the kingdom. 'The Abyssinians imprison their
political prisoners on inaccessible mountains, which are called
Ambas. They are of three descriptions. First class, in
which the prisoner is hoisted up by means of a basket and
pullies, there being no possible road; second, in which there
is one road; third, in which there are two or three roads.
There is water and cultivable ground on these Ambas, and
on them the prisoners pass their existence, forgotten and in
meditation, till perhaps some new revolution may put them
on the throne.'—*Colonel Gordon in Central Africa,* p. 406.

P. 38, l. 18. *The sides.* Johnson perhaps had in his
thoughts Milton's description of Eden :—

> ' Thus was this place
> A happy rural seat of various view :
> Groves whose rich trees wept odorous gums and balm
> Others whose fruit burnished with golden rind
> Hung amiable, Hesperian fables true,
> If true, here only, and of delicious taste.
> Betwixt them lawns, or level downs, and flocks
> Grazing the tender herb were interposed,
> Or palmy hillock, or the flowery lap
> Of some irriguous valley spread her store,
> Flowers of all hue, and without thorn the rose.
>
> .   .   .   .
>
>   About them frisking played
> All beasts of th' earth, since wild, and of all chase
> In wood or wilderness, forest or den.'
>
> *Paradise Lost,* iv. 246 and 340.

l. 27. *the solemn elephant.* In *Troilus and Cressida*, Act i. sc. 2, Ajax is described as 'slow as the elephant.' Milton writes of 'the unwieldy elephant,' *Paradise Lost*, iv. 345; Pope of the 'half-reasoning elephant,' *Essay on Man*, i. 222. It is odd to find the same terms applied to the elephant and the nightingale; yet Milton writes:

> 'Nor then the solemn nightingale
> Ceased warbling!'   *Paradise Lost*, vii. 435.

P. 39, l. 25. *solstitial rains.* It is only at the summer solstice that the rains fall. See *ante*, p. 37, l. 13.

l. 26. *reparation.* 'Reparation. 1. The act of repairing. 2. Supply of what is wasted. 3. Recompense for any injury; amends.'—Johnson's *Dictionary*.

P. 41, l. 33. *I long* ... Boswell one day recorded in his Journal :—'I was happy when tea came. Such, I take it, is the state of those who live in the country. Meals are wished for from the cravings of vacuity of mind as well as from the desire of eating.'—Boswell's *Life of Johnson*, v. 159.

P. 42, l. 4. *lutanist.* In Richardson's *Dictionary* examples are given of *lutanist, lutenist, lutinist*, and *lutist.*

l. 6. *I can discover* ... Cf. *Eccles.* ii. 1–11. Like the Preacher, Rasselas having proved his heart with pleasure, and not withheld it from any joy, had to own, 'Behold, all was vanity and vexation of spirit, and there was no profit under the sun.'

l. 7. *Proper pleasure*, i. e. its peculiar pleasure; the pleasure which belongs to it, and to it alone.

l. 16. *burthened with myself.*

> 'Pressed by the load of life the weary mind
> Surveys the general toil of human kind.'
>   Johnson, *Prologue to The Good Natured Man.*

l. 17. *I have*, &c. :—

> 'The lamb thy riot dooms to bleed to-day,
> Had he thy reason would he skip and play?
> Pleased to the last he crops the flowery food,
> And licks the hand just raised to shed his blood.
> Oh, blindness to the future! kindly given,
> That each may fill the circle marked by heaven.'
>   Pope, *Essay on Man*, i. 81.

l. 26. *some solace.* '"Depend upon it," said Johnson, "that if a man *talks* of his misfortunes there is something in them that is not disagreeable to him ; for where there is nothing but pure misery there never is any recourse to the mention of it."'—Boswell's *Life of Johnson*, iv. 31.

P. 43, l. 3. *imagining . . .* In like manner Polonius 'imagined that he had made himself acquainted with' Hamlet's 'disease of mind,' who, in his turn, 'considers him as one whose intellects were exhausted.' Johnson, in an admirable note on *Hamlet*, Act ii. sc. 4, says :—'This idea of dotage encroaching upon wisdom will solve all the phenomena of the character of Polonius.'

l. 7. *intellects.* Johnson, in his *Dictionary*, gives no example of this use of *intellect* in the plural. Boswell represents him as saying :—'There is a wicked inclination in most people to suppose an old man decayed in his intellects.' —*Life of Johnson*, iv. 181.

P. 44, l. 9. *hide me from myself.*

> 'Hide me, oh hide me from upbraiding Greece ;
>   Oh ! hide me from myself!'   Johnson, *Irene*, Act v. sc. 3.

l. 21. *Sir, said he, . . .* So when in *Cymbeline* Belarius had tried to make the young princes believe that they were happier in their forest life, Guiderius answers :—

> 'Haply this life is best,
> If quiet life be best ; sweeter to you
> That have a sharper known ; well corresponding
> With your stiff age ; but unto us it is
> A cell of ignorance.'   *Cymbeline*, Act iii. sc. 3, l. 29.

P. 45, l. 4. *we less regard others.* 'Custom so far regulates the sentiments at least of common minds that I believe men may be generally observed to grow less tender as they advance in age.'—Johnson, *Rambler*, No. 78.

P. 46, l. 4. *twenty months.* Johnson recorded on the birthday which saw him fifty-five years old: 'I have now spent fifty-five years in resolving, having from the earliest time almost that I can remember been forming schemes of a better life. I have done nothing.'—Boswell's *Life of Johnson*, i. 483.

P. 47, l. 28. *These* . . . . 'I believe most men may review all the lives that have passed within their observation without remembering one efficacious resolution, or being able to tell a single instance of a course of practice suddenly changed in consequence of a change of opinion, or an establishment of determination.'—Johnson, *Idler*, No. 27.

P. 48, l. 14. *grate.* 'Grate. 1. A partition made with bars placed near to one another, or crossing other: such as are in cloisters or prisons. 2. The range of bars within which fires are made.'—Johnson's *Dictionary*. Here it is used in the sense of cage, of which I cannot find any instance. Mrs. Barbauld, in *The Mouse's Petition*, makes the mouse say :

> 'For here forlorn and sad I sit,
> Within the wiry grate.'

But *within a grate* or *within the walls* is not the same as *in a grate* or *in the walls*.

l. 28. *blessing of hope.* 'It is necessary to hope, though hope should always be deluded ; for hope itself is happiness, and its frustrations, however frequent, are less dreadful than its extinction.'—Johnson, *Idler*, No. 58.

P. 49, l. 23. *By a wheel* . . . . Johnson was perhaps thinking of the great water-wheels at Marly, constructed in 1685, by which Versailles and St. Cloud were supplied with water.

P. 50, l. 16. *wings.* In 1784, the year in which the first balloon ascent was made in England, Johnson wrote : 'It is very seriously true that a subscription of £800 has been raised for the wire and workmanship of iron wings.'—Boswell's *Life of Johnson*, iv. 356, *n.* 1.

P. 51, l. 13. *You, sir* . . . . 'The philosopher hovering in the sky' would be whirled round with the country from which he had ascended. Whether Johnson himself shared in the artist's ignorance of this fact is not quite clear. The nature of the objection that he puts in the prince's mouth seems to show that he did.

l. 24. *the Nile.* 'With regard to the sources of the Nile,' wrote Herodotus (Bk. ii. ch. 28) more than twenty-three centuries ago, 'I have found no one among all those with whom I have conversed, whether Egyptians, Libyans, or Greeks, who professed to have any knowledge except a single person.' It was not till the year 1858 that the chief source of the Nile was discovered by Speke in the Victoria Nyanza. In 1862 he completed his discovery by reaching the Ripon Falls.

P. 52, l. 1. *Nothing* ... 'Johnson observed that so many objections might be made to everything that nothing could overcome them but the necessity of doing something. No man would be of any profession, as simply opposed to not being of it; but every one must do something.'—Boswell's *Life of Johnson*, ii. 128.

l. 4. *volant.* Johnson, in his *Dictionary*, quotes from Wilkins's *Math. Magick*: 'The volant, or flying automata, are such mechanical contrivances as have a self-motion, whereby they are carried aloft in the air, like birds.' *Volant* is used by Milton in the sense of *nimble, active*: 'His volant touch,' *Paradise Lost*, xi. 561. In *Henry V*, Act iii. sc. 7, the Dauphin, prancing his horse, says, 'Ça, ha! he bounds from the earth, as if his entrails were hairs; le cheval volant, the Pegasus.'

l. 34. *contagion of his confidence.*

'When first the college-rolls receive his name,
The young enthusiast quits his ease for fame;
Through all his veins the fever of renown
Spreads from the strong contagion of the gown.'
Johnson, *The Vanity of Human Wishes*, l. 135.
See *ante*, p. 119, l. 21, 'the contagion of misery.'

P. 53, l. 7. *half-dead.* Johnson is content with giving the artist a ducking. Voltaire would have crippled him for life at the very least; most likely would have killed him on the spot.

P. 54, l. 2. *Imlac.* 'Imlac in *Rasselas* I spelt with a *c* at the end, because it is less like English, which should always have the Saxon *k* added to the *c*.'—Boswell's *Life of Johnson*, iv. 31.

l. 11. *curiosity.* 'A generous and elevated mind is distinguished by nothing more certainly than an eminent degree of curiosity ; nor is that curiosity ever more agreeably or usefully employed than in examining the laws and customs of foreign nations.'—Johnson, *Dedication to Lobo's Abyssinia.* 'Curiosity is one of the permanent and certain characteristics of a vigorous intellect.'—*Rambler*, No. 103.

l. 30. *To talk in public.* . . . Johnson is here describing his own life. 'He seemed to me,' wrote the Rev. Dr. Maxwell, 'to be considered as a kind of public oracle, whom everybody thought they had a right to visit and consult.'— Boswell's *Life of Johnson*, ii. 118, and *ante*, p. 15.

P. 55, l. 4. *Goiama.* Lobo (p. 97) says that Goiama was 'one of the most fruitful provinces of all the Abyssinian dominions.' The fountain of the Nile, which he visited, he describes as 'two holes each about two feet diameter, a stone's cast distant from each other ; 'tis believed here that these springs are the vents of a great subterraneous lake.'— *Ib.* p. 98. Herodotus's informant placed the fountains of the Nile between Syene, a city of the Thebais, and Elephantine.— Bk. ii. ch. 28.

l. 6. *Africk.* Johnson, in his translation of Lobo, writes *Africa* or *Africk* indifferently.

l. 26. *Subordination* . . .

> 'Order is heaven's first law ; and this confest,
> Some are, and must be, greater than the rest.'
>
> Pope, *Essay on Man*, iv. 49.

P. 56, l. 13. *However* . . . 'When I, in a low-spirited fit, was talking to him with indifference of the pursuits which generally engage us in a course of action, and inquiring a *reason* for taking so much trouble ; " Sir," said he, in an animated tone, " it is driving on the system of life." '—Boswell's *Life of Johnson*, iv. 112. See *ante*, p. 113, l. 27.

l. 20. *invention.* One of Johnson's definitions of *to invent* is 'to make by the imagination.' It is in this sense that *invention* is here used.

P. 58, l. 3. *world of waters.*

> 'The rising World of waters dark and deep.'
>
> *Paradise Lost*, iii. 11.

l. 7. *barren uniformity.* The poets had not yet begun to
sing the praises of the sea. Mountains were still dreadful
and desolate, and the sea barren and uniform. A curious
passage in the *Travels* of W. Lithgow, who began his wan-
derings in the year 1609, shows how differently men looked
upon the wildness of nature. He says :—'Neare unto the
house of the Bishop of Eden on Libanus falleth precipitately
a great torrent over the sassinous bank, that maketh a
grevious noise night and day ; which, as I told him, me-
thought it should turn the Bishop *Surdo*, or stark deaf. But
the homely and simple man (not puft with ambition, greed,
and glorious apparel, like to our proud prelates of Christendom) told me, that continual custome brought him to depose
upon the day, and sleep better in the night because of the
sounding waters.'— Lithgow's *Travels*, ed. 1692, p. 188.
Johnson often enlarged upon the wretchedness of a sea-life.
'Why, Sir,' said he, 'no man will be a sailor who has contrivance enough to get himself into a jail ; for being in a
ship is being in a jail with the chance of being drowned.'—
Boswell's *Life of Johnson*, v. 137.

P. 58, l. 23. *naval.* Johnson defines *naval* as ' 1. con-
sisting of ships ; 2. belonging to ships.' The present use of
the word seems to be confined to ships of war.

P. 59, l. 24. *the great Mogul.* 'Akbar the Great, the
real founder of the Mughal empire as it existed for two centuries, was the contemporary of our own Queen Elizabeth ...
Aurangzeb's long reign, from 1658 to 1707, may be regarded
as representing both the culminating point of Mughal power
and the beginning of its decay. . . . In 1739 Nadir Shah of
Persia, the sixth and last of the great Mahometan conquerors
of India, swept like a whirlwind over Hindustan. Thence-
forth the Great Mughal (Mogul) became a mere name,
though the hereditary succession continued unbroken down
to our own day. . . . Last of all [the lineal heirs of the Mughal
line] came Bahadur Shah, who atoned for his association
with the mutineers in 1857 by banishment to Burmah. Thus
ended the Mughal line, after a history which covers 330
years.'— *Encycl. Brit.*, ninth ed., xii. 794–6.

P. 60, l. 2. *and though* . . . Johnson, after his interview with George III, who did not 'utter anything above the power of a common man,' said : 'Sir, they may talk of the king as they will, but he is the finest gentleman I have ever seen.'—Boswell's *Life of Johnson*, ii. 40.

l. 20. *accommodations.* Johnson defines *accommodation* in the plural as 'conveniences, things requisite to ease or refreshment.' It was a favourite word with him. See *ante*, p. 86, l. 12.

l. 28. *and who* . . . See *post*, p. 191, note on p. 126, l. 21.

P. 61, l. 4. *veneration.* 'The chief glory of every people arises from its authors.'—Johnson's *Works*, v. 49.

l. 11. *novelty.* Goldsmith complained 'that he had come too late into the world, for that Pope and other poets had taken up the places in the Temple of Fame ; so that, as but a few at any period can possess poetical reputation, a man of genius can now hardly acquire it.'—Boswell's *Life of Johnson*, ii. 358. 'St. Jerome relates that his preceptor, Donatus, explaining that sensible passage in Terence, *Nihil est dictum quod non sit dictum prius*, railed severely at the ancients for taking from him his best thoughts. *Pereant qui ante nos nostra dixerunt.*'—Dr. Warton, *Essay on Pope*, i. 88.

l. 17. *transcription* . . . Johnson, in his *Life of Dryden*, attributes this 'transcription' to indolence or inattention. 'New arts,' he says, 'are long in the world before poets describe them ; for they borrow everything from their predecessors, and commonly derive very little from nature or from life.'—*Works*, vii. 316.

l. 20. *that the first* . . . 'The chief talent of Virgil was propriety of thoughts, and ornament of words ; Homer was rapid in his thoughts, and took all the liberties both of numbers and of expressions which his language and the age in which he lived allowed him. Homer's invention was more copious, Virgil's more confined.'—Dryden, *Preface to the Fables*.

l. 25. *the volumes.* 'Some mosques possess a collection of magnificent illuminated MSS., chiefly copies of the *Koran* and other religious books.'—*Encycl. Brit.*, ninth ed., xvi. 864.

P. 62, l. 29. *The business* ... 'The true ideal of landscape is precisely the same as that of the human form ; it is the expression of the specific—not the individual but the specific—characters of every object, in their perfection ; there is an ideal form of every herb, flower, and tree ; it is that form to which every individual of the species has a tendency to arrive, freed from the influence of accident or disease. ... Every herb and flower of the field has its specific, distinct, and perfect beauty ; it has its peculiar habitation, expression, and function. The highest art is that which seizes this specific character, which developes and illustrates it, which assigns to it its proper position in the landscape, and which by means of it enhances and enforces the great impression which the picture is intended to convey. ... It does not follow that because such accurate knowledge is *necessary* to the painter that (*sic*) it should constitute the painter ; nor that such knowledge is valuable in itself, and without reference to high ends. Every kind of knowledge may be sought from ignoble motives, and for ignoble ends ; and in those who so possess it it is ignoble knowledge ; while the very same knowledge is in another mind an attainment of the highest dignity, and conveying the greatest blessing. This is the difference between the mere botanist's knowledge of plants, and the great poet's or painter's knowledge of them. The one notes their distinctions for the sake of swelling his herbarium, the other that he may render them vehicles of expression and emotion.'—Ruskin, *Modern Painters*, 2nd ed., pp. xxxviii, xlvi, xlix.

P. 63, l. 7. *His character.* That is to say, his character as a poet.

l. 16. *transcendental.* Johnson defines *transcendental* in the sense in which he uses it here, as 'general ; pervading many particulars.'

l. 20. *posterity.* 'The warm desires, the long expectations of youth are founded on the ignorance of themselves and of the world ; they are gradually damped by time and experience, by disappointment and possession ; and after the middle season the crowd must be content to remain at the foot of the mountain, while the few who have climbed the summit aspire to descend or expect to fall.   In old age the consolation of hope is reserved for the tenderness of parents who commence a new life in their children ; . . . and the vanity of authors who presume the immortality of their names and writings.'—Gibbon, *Misc. Works*, i. 275.

l. 21. *legislator of mankind.*   Shakespeare may be looked upon as this legislator of mankind ; for, says Johnson, 'it may be doubted whether from all his successors more maxims of theoretical knowledge, or more rules of practical prudence can be collected than he alone has given to his country.'—*Works*, v. 131.

P. 64, l. 25. *By what means* . . .   Boswell, describing a trip that he took with Johnson in June, 1781, says, 'he talked little to us in the carriage, being chiefly occupied in reading . . . his own *Prince of Abyssinia*, on which he seemed to be intensely fixed ; having told us that he had not looked at it since it was first published.   I happened to take it out of my pocket this day, and he seized upon it with avidity.   He pointed out to me the following remarkable passage [the passage that begins ' By what means' and ends ' Supreme Being'].   He said, "This, Sir, no man can explain otherwise."'—Boswell's *Life of Johnson*, iv. 119.

P. 65, l. 7. *mighty confluence* . . .   ' The streets of Jerusalem at Easter present a strange spectacle from the numerous national costumes seen together.   The European tourist, the Turkish nizam, the hooded Armenian, the long-haired Greek monk, are mingled with the native peasants in yellow turbans and striped mantles, with Armenian pilgrims wearing broad red sashes, Jews in Oriental costume or with the fur cap and lovelocks of the Pharisee, Russians in knee boots and padded robes, and native ladies in white mantles with black face veils.   The architecture of the city, Oriental, Gothic, Byzantine, or Italian, tells the same story—that Jerusalem has been for eighteen centuries a holy city in the eyes of Jew, Christian, and Moslem alike, and the religious centre of half the world.'—*Encycl. Brit.*, ninth ed., xiii. 644.

l. 28. *Yet since men* . . .   ' We were now treading that illus-

trious island [Iona] which was once the luminary of the Cale-
donian regions, whence savage clans and roving barbarians
derived the benefits of knowledge, and the blessings of
religion. To abstract the mind from all local emotion would
be impossible, if it were endeavoured, and would be foolish,
if it were possible. Whatever withdraws us from the power
of our senses ; whatever makes the past, the distant, or the
future predominate over the present, advances us in the
dignity of thinking beings. Far from me and from my friends
be such frigid philosophy as may conduct us indifferent and
unmoved over any ground which has been dignified by
wisdom, bravery, or virtue. That man is little to be envied
whose patriotism would not gain force upon the plain of
Marathon, or whose piety would not grow warmer among
the ruins of Iona.' — Johnson, *A Journey to the Hebrides.*
Works, ix. 145.

l. 32. *our religion.* 'The Christianity professed by the
Abyssins is so corrupted with superstitions, errors, and
heresies, and so mingled with ceremonies borrowed from
the Jews, that little besides the name of Christianity is to be
found here.'—Lobo's *Abyssinia,* p. 47.

l. 34. *That the* ... 'It may be dangerous to receive too
readily, and indulge too fondly, opinions from which perhaps
no pious mind is wholly disengaged, of local sanctity and
local devotion. You know what strange effects they have
produced over a great part of the Christian world. I am
now writing, and you, when you read this, are reading under
the Eye of Omnipresence. To what degree fancy is to be
admitted into religious offices it would require much deliberation to determine. I am far from intending totally to exclude
it. . . . We may allow Fancy to suggest certain ideas in
certain places ; but Reason must always be heard when she
tells us that those ideas and those places have no natural or
necessary relation. When we enter a church we habitually
recall to mind the duty of adoration, but we must not omit
adoration for want of a temple ; because we know, and ought
to remember, that the Universal Lord is everywhere present,
and that therefore to come to Iona or to Jerusalem, though it

may be useful, cannot be necessary.'—Boswell's *Life of Johnson*, ii. 276.

P. 66, l. 14. *There is* ... 'How evil came into the world; for what reason it is that life is overspread with such bound-less varieties of misery; why the only thinking being of this globe is doomed to think merely to be wretched, and to pass his time from youth to age in fearing or in suffering calamities, is a question which philosophers have long asked, and which philosophy could never answer.'—Johnson, *Idler*, No. 89.

l. 16. *Knowledge* ... Johnson, one day in a boat on the Thames, talking with Boswell on the advantage of knowledge, 'called to the boy [who was rowing them], "What would you give, my lad, to know about the Argonauts?" "Sir," said the boy, "I would give what I have." Johnson was much pleased with his answer, and we gave him a double fare. Dr. John-son, then turning to me, "Sir," said he, "a desire of know-ledge is the natural feeling of mankind; and every human being, whose mind is not debauched, will be willing to give all that he has to get knowledge."'—Boswell's *Life of Johnson*, i. 458.

l. 32. *communication between distant places.* Yet Johnson, tenderly attached though he was to his mother, never returned to Lichfield to visit her, though she lived more than twenty-one years after his removal to London. Measured by time London, so late as 1772, was one hour farther from Lichfield than it now is from Marseilles. According to Horace Walpole (*Memoirs of the Reign of George III*, iv. 327), 'George III had never seen the sea, nor ever been thirty miles from London at the age of thirty-four.'

l. 34. *public inconveniences.* Johnson gives instances in the next line of these 'public inconveniences' in the mountains and rivers that obstruct roads.

P. 67, l. 1. *roads.* Arthur Young, writing in 1768 of the roads in the north-west of England, says: 'I would advise all travellers to consider the country between Newcastle-under-Line and Preston as sea, and as soon think of driving into the ocean as venturing into such detestable roads.' On the road from Wigan to Preston he 'met with ruts four feet deep, and floating with mud only from a wet summer.'—*Tour through the North of England*, iv. 431-5.

l. 10. *Human life* . . . 'Philosophers there are,' wrote Johnson, 'who try to make themselves believe that this life is happy, but they believe it only while they are saying it, and never yet produced conviction in a single mind.'—*Piozzi Letters*, i. 150. See *post*, p. 195, note on p. 144, l. 13.

l. 28. *life glide away.*

> 'An age that melts with unperceived decay,
>   And glides in modest innocence away.'
>
> > *The Vanity of Human Wishes*, l. 293.

P. 68, l. 7. *Often* . . . 'The man of business wearied with unsatisfactory prosperity retires to the town of his nativity and expects to play away the last years with the companions of his childhood, and recover youth in the fields where he once was young.'—Johnson, *The Idler*, No. 43.

l. 22. *secrecy of solitude.* Boswell thus describes London : 'There, and there alone, a man's own house is truly his *castle*, in which he can be in perfect safety from intrusion whenever he pleases. I never shall forget how well this was expressed to me one day by Mr. Meynell: "The chief advantage of London (said he) is that a man is always *so near his burrow.*" '—*Life of Johnson*, iii. 378. Gibbon (*Misc. Works*, ii. 291) wrote of London : 'La liberté d'un simple particulier se fortifie par l'immensité de la ville.'

l. 33. *But I was* . . . Johnson thus describes his first return to Lichfield after his long absence in London : 'Last winter I went down to my native town, where I found the streets much narrower and shorter than I thought I had left them, inhabited by a new race of people to whom I was very little known. My play-fellows were grown old, and forced me to suspect that I was no longer young. My only remaining friend has changed his principles.'—Boswell's *Life of Johnson*, i. 370.

P. 69, l. 9. *a school.* It is probable that the school which Imlac opened was like the school of declamation described on p. 82, l. 6.

l. 28. *I am* ... The young forest-bred prince in *Cymbeline* feels this strongly when he says :—

> 'What should we speak of
> When we are old as you ? When we shall hear
> The rain and wind beat dark December, how,
> In this our pinching cave, shall we discourse
> The freezing hours away? We have seen nothing.'
>
> *Cymbeline*, Act. iii. sc. 3.

P. 72, l. 9. *knowledge* ... 'Then said I, Wisdom is better than strength.'—*Ecclesiastes* ix. 16.

l. 17. *It has* ...

> 'See him from nature rising slow to art !
> To copy instinct then was reason's part ;
> Thus then to man the voice of nature spake,
> Go, from the creatures thy instructions take :
> Learn from the birds what food the thickets yield ;
> Learn from the beasts the physic of the field ;
> Thy arts of building from the bee receive ;
> Learn of the mole to plough, the worm to weave ;
> Learn of the little nautilus to sail,
> Spread the thin oar, and catch the driving gale.'
>
> Pope, *Essay on Man*, iii. 169.

P. 73, l. 12. *He that* ... 'Johnson was all his life fond of computation, as it fixed his attention steadily upon something without, and prevented his mind from preying upon itself.'—Boswell's *Life of Johnson*, i. 72. He calculated the number of verses that he must read every Sunday to go through the Scriptures in a year.—*Ib.*, *n.* 2. In the calculation in the text he must have reckoned vigorous walking at the rate of a little over three miles an hour. At the rate of four miles an hour the distance would have been completed in less than five years and a half.

l. 22. *a prey to superstition.* 'Johnson was prone to superstition, but not to credulity.'—Boswell's *Life of Johnson*, iv. 426. He was willing, nay, he was anxious, to believe in supernatural things as 'an evidence for spirit' (*ib.* ii. 150), but in each instance that was brought before him, sifting as he did the evidence rigorously, he was never convinced. Of second-sight he wrote on his return from the Hebrides :—

' I never could advance my curiosity to conviction, but came away at last only willing to believe.'—*Ib.* ii. 10, *n.* 3.

P. 76, l. 25. *the ruggedness* ... Johnson, writing of the booksellers with whom Dryden had to deal, says: ' The general conduct of traders was much less liberal in those times than in our own; their views were narrower, and their manners grosser. To the mercantile ruggedness of that race the delicacy of the poet was sometimes exposed.'—*Works*, vii. 299.

P. 77, l. 10. *As they* ... William Lithgow (*ante* p. 167) thus describes Cairo :—' This incorporate world of Grand Cairo is the most admirable and greatest city seen upon the earth, being thrice as large of bounds as Constantinople, and likewise so populous, but not so well builded, being situate in a pleasant plain, and in the heart of Egypt, kissing Nilus at some parts ... There is a great commerce here with exceeding many nations, for by their concurring hither it is wonderfully peopled with infinite numbers ... In this town a traveller may ever happily find all these sorts of Christians, Italians, French, Greeks, Chelfaines, Georgians, Ethiopians, Jacobins, Syrians, Armenians, Nicolaitans, Abyssines, Cypriots, Sclavonians, Captivate Maltezes, Sicilians, Albaneses, and High Hungarians, Ragusans, and their own Egyptian Coptis; the number of which is thought to be beyond two hundred thousand : besides the infinite number of Infidels, whose sorts are these : Turks, Tawny Moors, White Moors, Black Moors or Negroes, Musilmans, Tartars, Persians, Indians, Sabuncks, Berdoanes, Jews, Arabians, Barbares, and Tingitanian Saracens. All of which are Mahometans and idolatrous Pagans.'—Lithgow's *Travels*, ed. 1692, pp. 291, 293.

P. 78, l. 4. *His table* ... ' The inhabitants here [in Cairo] were the first inventors of the mathematical sciences, of letters, and of the use of writing, great magicians and astrologians, and are yet endued with a special dexterity of wit; but somewhat slothful, and given to riot and luxury; merry also, great singers and sociable companions.'—Lithgow's *Travels*, p. 295.

P. 79, l. 12 *when you feel* ... 'Who is there of those who frequent these luxurious assemblies that will not confess his own uneasiness, or cannot recount the vexations and distresses that prey upon the lives of his gay companions? The world in its best state is nothing more than a larger assembly of beings, combining to counterfeit happiness which they do not feel.'—Johnson, *The Adventurer*, No. 120.

l. 29. *The causes* ... 'Such is life, that whatever is proposed it is much easier to find reasons for rejecting than embracing.'—Johnson, *The Rambler*, No. 39. ' " No man," Johnson said, " would be of any profession as simply opposed to not being of it; but every one must do something." '—Boswell's *Life of Johnson*, ii. 128. Even when man does choose, he rarely chooses wisely.

> 'How rarely reason guides the stubborn choice,
> Rules the bold hand, or prompts the suppliant voice.'
> *The Vanity of Human Wishes*, l. 11.

P. 80, l. 5. *Very few* ... Johnson, writing to Boswell about the choice of a profession, said : 'Life is not long, and too much of it must not pass in idle deliberation how it shall be spent ; deliberation which those who begin it by prudence and continue it with subtlety must, after long expense of thought, conclude by chance. To prefer one future mode of life to another upon just reasons requires faculties which it has not pleased our Creator to give us.'—Boswell's *Life of Johnson*, ii. 22. ' " Young man," said Omar, "it is of little use to form plans of life ... With an insatiable thirst for knowledge I trifled away the years of improvement; with a restless desire of seeing different countries I have always resided in the same city; with the highest expectation of connubial felicity I have lived unmarried ; and with unalterable resolutions of contemplative retirement, I am going to die within the walls of Bagdat." '—Johnson, *The Idler*, No. 101.

l. 26. *images.* Johnson defines *to image* 'to copy by the fancy; to imagine.' *Images*, therefore, may mean products of the fancy or of the imagination; but in his *Dictionary* he gives no instance of the word thus used.

P. 81, l. 10. *The first years* ... Johnson is preaching on the old, old text : 'Remember now thy Creator in the days of thy youth, while the evil days come not, nor the years draw nigh when thou shalt say, I have no pleasure in them.' —*Ecclesiastes* xii. 1.

l. 14. *life short or miserable.* Shortness of life Johnson held a far greater evil than misery of life. He said : 'Mere existence is so much better than nothing that one would rather exist even in pain than not exist.'—Boswell's *Life of Johnson*, iii. 295.

l. 23. *the maladies . . .* The opposite of all this was the case of Adam in *As You Like It* (Act ii. sc. 3. l. 47), who says :—

> 'Though I look old, yet I am strong and lusty ;
> For in my youth I never did apply
> Hot and rebellious liquors in my blood,
> Nor did not with unbashful forehead woo
> The means of weakness and debility ;
> Therefore my age is as a lusty winter,
> Frosty but kindly.'

l. 30. *the horror of derision.* Johnson forcibly expressed this *horror* when he said, 'Ah, Sir ! a boy's being flogged is not so severe as a man's having the hiss of the world against him.'—Boswell's *Life of Johnson*, i. 451.

P. 82, l. 19. *He compared . . .* Many years later Johnson 'called Mr. Pitt [the first Earl of Chatham] a meteor ; Sir Robert Walpole a fixed star.'—Boswell's *Life of Johnson*, v. 339.

P. 84, l. 6. *Young man . . .* In Fielding's *Joseph Andrews*, which Johnson had never read, there is a passage very like this : Parson Adams had scarcely finished an exhortation on patience and resignation, when a false report reached him that his little boy was drowned. 'He stood silent a moment, and soon began to stamp about the room and deplore his loss with the bitterest agony. Joseph . . . endeavoured to comfort the parson, in which attempt he used many arguments that he had at several times remembered out of his own discourses, both in private and public (for he was a great enemy to the passions, and preached nothing

more than the conquest of them by reason and grace), but he
was not at leisure now to hearken to his advice. " Child,
child," said he, " do not go about impossibilities." '—*Joseph
Andrews*, Bk. iv. ch. 8. Burton, in his *Anatomy of Melancholy*, ed. 1660, p. 70, says :—' They that teach wisdom,
patience, meekness are the veriest dizards, hairbrains, and
most discontent.' *Dizard* or *dizzard* is defined by Johnson
as ' a blockhead ; a fool.'

l. 15. *The prince* . . . Could a Prince of Abyssinia have
read Shakespeare he might have learnt the same lesson from
Leonato in *Much Ado about Nothing :*—

> 'Leonato.   For, brother, men
>   Can counsel and speak comfort to that grief
>   Which they themselves not feel ; but, tasting it,
>   Their counsel turns to passion, which before
>   Would give preceptial medicine to rage,
>   Fetter strong madness in a silken thread,
>   Charm ache with air and agony with words :
>   No, no ; 'tis all men's office to speak patience
>   To those that wring under the load of sorrow,
>   But no man's virtue nor sufficiency
>   To be so moral when he shall endure
>   The like himself. Therefore give me no counsel :
>   My griefs cry louder than advertisement.
> Antonio. Therein do men from children nothing differ.
> Leonato. I pray thee, peace. I will be flesh and blood ;
>   For there was never yet philosopher
>   That could endure the toothache patiently,
>   However they have writ the style of gods
>   And made a push at chance and sufferance.'
>
>   Act v. sc. 1. l. 20.

P. 85, l. 8. *They were* . . . Johnson, writing of the High-
landers, among whom he travelled in the year 1773, says :
' They have inquired and considered little, and do not always
feel their own ignorance. They are not much accustomed
to be interrogated by others, and seem never to have thought
upon interrogating themselves.'—*Works*, ix. 114. Voltaire,
in his *Histoire d'un bon Bramin*, after describing the
condition of a man whose wisdom was his sorrow, con-

tinues : ' Je vis le même jour la vieille femme qui demeurait
dans son voisinage : je lui demandai si elle avait jamais été
affligée de ne savoir pas comment son âme était faite. Elle
ne comprit seulement pas ma question ; elle n'avait jamais
réfléchi un seul moment de sa vie sur un seul des points qui
tourmentaient le bramin.'

l. 23. *She hoped* . . . Johnson, in his *Life of Gay*, thus
ridicules that pastoral life for which the princess longed.
'There is something in the poetical Arcadia so remote from
known reality and speculative possibility, that we can never
support its representation through a long work. A pastoral
of a hundred lines may be endured ; but who will hear of
sheep and goats, and myrtle bowers, and purling rivulets
through five acts ? Such scenes please barbarians in the
dawn of literature, and children in the dawn of life ; but will
be for the most part thrown away as men grow wise and
nations grow learned.'—*Works*, viii. 71.

P. 86, l. 3. *The shrubs* . . . Johnson is here describing
the landscape-gardening that was in fashion in his time. In
his *Life* of his contemporary Shenstone, he tells how that
poet 'began to point his prospects, to diversify his surface, to
entangle his walks, and to wind his waters.'—*Works*, viii. 409.

l. 12. *accommodations.* See *ante*, p. 168, note on p. 60, l. 20.

P. 87, l. 2. *Bassa.* Johnson, in his *Dictionary*, under
Bassa refers to Bashaw. '*Pasha, Pacha.* Also *bashaw*,
Persian báshá, bádsháh, a governor of a province, great lord ;
lit. 'protecting the king.' Persian, pád, protecting ; sháh.
king.'—Skeat's *Etym. Dict.*

i. 9. **riot.** *Riot*, a favourite word with Johnson, is defined
by him as ' 1. to revel ; 2. to luxuriate ; 3. to banquet luxu-
riously ; 4. to raise a sedition or uproar.' It is in the first
sense that he uses the word here, and *ante*, p. 140, l. 26. It
is in this sense that it is used in *Romans* xiii. 13 :—' Let us
walk honestly as in the day ; not in rioting and drunken-
ness.' See *ante*, p. 162, note on p. 42, l. 17, for an instance of
the word as used by Pope.

l. 27. *apartments.* The French word *appartement*, from
which *apartment* is derived, is defined by Littré as *logement*

composé de plusieurs pièces. Johnson in his *Dictionary* defines *Apartment* as ' A part of the house allotted to the use
of any particular person ; a *room* ; a *set of rooms.*' The
latter meaning, which was passing away in his time, is now
altogether lost.

P. 88, l. 15. *His discourse* . . . These balanced epithets
are too common in Johnson and his imitators. Cf. *ante,*
p. 134, l. 29.

P. 89, l. 17. *I am sometimes* . . . ' I said to the Lady
Abbess of a convent, Madam, you are here, not for the love
of virtue, but the fear of vice. She said she should remember
this as long as she lived.'—Boswell's *Life of Johnson,* ii. 435.

l. 27. *The life* . . . ' " I never read of a hermit," said Johnson, "but in imagination I kiss his feet ; never of a monastery,
but I could fall on my knees and kiss the pavement. But I
think putting young people there who know nothing of life,
nothing of retirement, is dangerous and wicked." '—Boswell's
Life of Johnson, v. 62. Southey (*Life of Wesley,* i. 39)
writes :—' Some time before John Wesley's return to the
University he had travelled many miles to see what is called
" a serious man." This person said to him, " Sir, you wish
to serve God and go to heaven. Remember, you cannot
serve Him alone ; you must therefore *find* companions or
make them ; the Bible knows nothing of solitary religion."
Wesley never forgot these words.' See *post,* p. 198, note on
p. 152, l. 6.

P. 90, l. 2. *The happiness* . . . Rousseau had published
his *Discourse on the Origin of Inequality* in 1754. Mr.
Morley, writing of it, says :—' Rousseau thought and talked
about the state of nature, because all his world was thinking
and talking about it. He used phrases and formulas with
reference to it, which other people used. He required no
more evidence than they did as to the reality of the existence
of the supposed set of conditions to which they gave the
almost sacramental name of state of nature. He never
thought of asking, any more than anybody else did in the
middle of the eighteenth century, what sort of proof, how
strong, how direct, was to be had, that primeval man had

such and such habits, and changed them in such a way and direction, and for such reasons.'—Morley's *Rousseau*, ed. 1878, p. 104. 'We have never seen in our own generation —indeed, the world has not seen more than once or twice in all the course of history—a literature which has exercised such prodigious influence over the minds of men, over every cast and shade of intellect, as that which emanated from Rousseau between 1749 and 1762. . . . Now in all the speculations of Rousseau, the central figure . . . is uniformly Man, in a supposed state of nature. Every law or institution which would misbeseem this imaginary being under these ideal circumstances is to be condemned as having lapsed from an original perfection.'—Maine's *Ancient Law*, fifth ed., p. 87. 'It is a well-known saying of Napoleon, that if Rousseau had never lived there would have been no French Revolution; and in spite of its manifest exaggeration there is a sense in which this saying is not without plausibility.'— Lecky's *History of England*, v. 345. Johnson said of Rousseau :—' "Rousseau *knows* he is talking nonsense, and laughs at the world for staring at him." BOSWELL. "How so, Sir?" JOHNSON. "Why, Sir, a man who talks nonsense so well must know that he is talking nonsense." '—Boswell's *Life of Johnson*, ii. 74.

l. 19. *One of the youngest.* . . . Johnson implies that it is those who are most ignorant of the world, the young, that is to say, who are most apt to suspect hypocrisy. 'The truth is,' he says, ' that there is very little hypocrisy in the world ; we do not so often endeavour or wish to impose on others as on ourselves.'—*The Idler*, No. 27.

P. 91, l. 12. *The way.* . . . In Fielding's *Tom Jones*, which was published ten years before *Rasselas*, this philosopher finds his counterpart in the philosopher Square, who 'measured all actions by the unalterable rule of right, and the eternal fitness of things.'—*Tom Jones*, Bk. iii. ch. 3.

P. 92, l. 24. *as he was yet young.* Rasselas by this time was about thirty-two. He is in his twenty-sixth year at the opening of the story, *ante*, p. 41, l. 2 ; he passes twenty months ' in visionary bustle,' *ante*, p. 46, l. 4 ; and

four months 'in resolving to lose no more time in idle
resolves,' *ante*, p. 47, l. 29. Ten months he spent in 'fruitless researches' for a means of escape, *ante*, p. 48, l. 30;
and a year with the inventor of the wings, *ante*, p. 53, l. 1.
Some months, perhaps a year, must be given to his conver-
sations with Imlac, to digging the outlet, and to the journey
to Cairo. In that town they studied the language two years
(*ante*, p. 78, l. 15) before they began their 'experiments upon
life.' That Shakespeare makes Hamlet thirty years old
often raises wonder. It is more surprising that Rasselas
should be represented as thirty-two.

P. 93, l. 30. *Yet, since* . . . 'JOHNSON. "I agree with
Mr. Boswell that there must be a high satisfaction in being
a feudal Lord; but we are to consider that we ought not to
wish to have a number of men unhappy for the satisfaction
of one." '—Boswell's *Life of Johnson*, ii. 178.

P. 94, l. 15. *At last.* . . . Johnson had thus described
the fall of Wolsey :—

> 'At length his sovereign frowns—the train of state
> Mark the keen glance, and watch the sign to hate.
> Where'er he turns he meets a stranger's eye,
> His suppliants scorn him, and his followers fly;
> Now drops at once the pride of awful state,
> The golden canopy, the glittering plate,
> The regal palace, the luxurious board,
> The liveried army, and the menial lord.'
>
> *The Vanity of Human Wishes*, l. 109,

l. 16. *Constantinople.* Egypt in the year 1517 became a
province of the Turkish empire. It is a province still, though
in most respects it is an independent power.

l. 25. *Janizaries.* According to Gibbon this famous troop
was raised by the Sultan Amurath the First, who reigned
from 1360 to 1389. He attacked and defeated the Sclavonian
nations between the Danube and the Adriatic. 'Many
thousands of the European captives were educated in religion
and arms; and the new militia was consecrated and named
by a celebrated dervish. Standing in the front of their
ranks, he stretched the sleeve of his gown over the head of

the foremost soldier, and his blessing was delivered in these
words :—" Let them be called Janizaries (*Yengi Cheri*, or new
soldiers) ; may their countenance be ever bright ! their hand
victorious ! their sword keen ! may their spear always hang
over the heads of their enemies ; and wheresoever they go,
may they return with a *white face* ! " Such was the origin of
these haughty troops, the terror of the nations, and sometimes
of the sultans themselves. Their valour has declined, their
discipline is relaxed, and their tumultuary array is incapable of
contending with the order and weapons of modern tactics; but
at the time of their institution they possessed a decisive superiority in war ; since a regular body of infantry, in constant
exercise and pay, was not maintained by any of the princes of
Christendom.' Milman, in a note on this passage, says that it
was Amurath's predecessor, Orchan, who was their founder.
—*Decline and Fall of the Roman Empire*, ed. 1862, viii. 29.
In Skeat's *Etym. Dict., Janizaries* is derived from *yeñi*, new ;
and *askari*, a soldier. 'White and black face,' says Gibbon,
' are common expressions of praise and reproach in the
Turkish language.' In the *Encycl. Brit.*, ninth ed., ii. 617, the
destruction of the Janizaries is thus described :—' From being
the sultan's slaves they became his masters, and the history
of Turkey shows a long list of rulers appointed, deposed, or
murdered by the Janissaries. Two attempts to break their
power failed disastrously. But Sultan Mahmoud II was not
daunted by a first failure, and when in 1826 he commenced
his reorganisation of the army, and the Janissaries again rose
against him, they found him prepared. The new troops
remained faithful, and in a terrible three days' struggle, in
which 20,000 of their number were killed, the Janissaries
as a body were annihilated.'

l. 30. *insinuated herself.* Johnson defines *to insinuate* in
this sense : 'to push gently into favour or regard.'

P. 95, l. 2. *airy.* Johnson defines *airy* in this sense as
'gay, sprightly, full of mirth.' He speaks of ' Mrs. Chol-
mondely, a very airy lady.'—Boswell's *Life of Johnson*, v.
248. See *post*, p. 193, note on p. 140, l. 5.

l. 32. '*Answer*,' *said she.* . . . Johnson, more than twenty

years later, criticising Gray's *Prospect of Eton College,* says:—
'His supplication to father Thames to tell him who drives
the hoop or tosses the ball is useless and puerile. Father
Thames has no better means of knowing than himself.'—
Works, viii. 483.

P. 96, l. 6. *our provinces. Province* in this sense is defined by Johnson, 'The proper office or business of anyone.'

l. 11. *ease among the poor.* Goldsmith, in *The Deserted
Village,* l. 5, published eleven years after *Rasselas,* describes
Auburn, as he had known it, as

> 'Dear lovely bowers of innocence and ease.'

Boswell, writing of Crabbe's poem, *The Village,* says:—'Its
sentiments as to the false notions of rustic happiness and
rustic virtue were quite congenial with Johnson's own.'—*Life
of Johnson,* iv. 175. Crabbe, in Book I of this poem, says:—

> 'I paint the cot
> As truth will paint it, and as Bards will not.
> Nor you, ye Poor, of lettered scorn complain;
> To you the smoothest song is smooth in vain;
> O'ercome by labour and bowed down by time,
> Feel you the barren flattery of a rhyme?'

Yet Burns, a year or two later, wrote in his *Epistle to Davie:*—

> 'To lye in kilns and barns at e'en,
> When banes are craz'd and bluid is thin,
>   Is doubtless great distress!
> Yet then content could make us blest;
> Ev'n then sometimes we'd snatch a taste
>   Of truest happiness.
>
> .   .   .   .   .   .
>
> But tent me, Davie, ace o' hearts!
> (To say aught less wad wrang the cartes,
>   And flatt'ry I detest)
> This life has joys for you and I;
> An' joys that riches ne'er could buy,
>   An' joys the very best.'

l. 13. *Poverty.* . . . 'There is no place,' said Johnson,
'where economy can be so well practised as in London. . . .
You cannot play tricks with your fortune in a small place; you
must make an uniform appearance. Here a lady may have

well-furnished apartments and elegant dress, without any meat in her kitchen.'—Boswell's *Life of Johnson*, iii. 378.

l. 15. *It is* . . . . 'To be idle and to be poor have always been reproaches, and therefore every man endeavours with his utmost care to hide his poverty from others, and his idleness from himself.'—Johnson, *The Idler*, No. 17.

l. 21. *Yet some* . . . . Johnson, in his undergraduate days, used to go to Christ Church and get some lectures at second-hand from his friend Taylor, 'till, his poverty being so extreme that his shoes were worn out, and his feet appeared through them, he saw that this humiliating circumstance was perceived by the Christ Church men, and he came no more. He was too proud to accept of money, and somebody having set a pair of new shoes at his door he threw them away with indignation.'—Boswell's *Life of Johnson*, i. 76.

l. 24. *and others.* . . . 'There are minds so impatient of inferiority that their gratitude is a species of revenge, and they return benefits, not because recompense is a pleasure, but because obligation is a pain.'—Johnson, *The Rambler*, No. 87.

P. 97, l. 8. *allayed.* Johnson defines *allay*, used in this sense, 'to join anything to another, so as to abate its predominant qualities.' *Allay*, as thus used, has been gradually displaced by the modern form *alloy*. Boswell, in reporting Johnson's talk, makes him say *unalloyed* (*post*, p. 199, note on p. 152, l. 20), but probably he uses the form of the word to which he himself was accustomed.

l. 28. *The old man* . . . Johnson said to Boswell: 'Young men have more virtue than old men; they have more generous sentiments in every respect.'—*Life of Johnson*, i. 445. See *ante*, p. 163, note on p. 45, l. 4.

l. 34. *to suspect.* The object of this verb is, of course, the same as the object of *to practise*—' it.'

P. 98, l. 2. *scrupulosity.* *Scrupulosity* was a favourite word with Johnson. 'You will be able,' wrote Sir W. Jones, 'to examine with the minutest *scrupulosity*, as Johnson would call it.'—Boswell's *Life of Johnson*, iv. 5, *n.* 2. See *ante*, p. 148, l. 16.

P. 100, l. 2. *If he.* ... Lewis XIV said :—'Toutes les fois que je donne une place vacante, je fais cent mécontens et un ingrat.'—Voltaire, *Siècle de Louis XIV*, ch. 26.

l. 26. *bribery of flattery.* 'When I boasted at Rasay of my independency of spirit, and that I could not be bribed, Dr. Johnson said, " Yes, you may be bribed by flattery." '— Boswell's *Life of Johnson*, v. 305.   Gay, in his *Fables*, No. 1, says :—

> 'Learn to contemn all praise betimes,
> For flattery's the nurse of crimes.'

P. 101, l. 1. *which I would.* ...

> 'How many thousand of my poorest subjects
> Are at this hour asleep ! O sleep, O gentle sleep,
> Nature's soft nurse, how have I frighted thee,
> That thou no more wilt weigh my eyelids down,
> And steep my senses in forgetfulness?
> Why rather, sleep, liest thou in smoky cribs,
> Upon uneasy pallets stretching thee
> And hushed with buzzing night-flies to thy slumber,
> Than in the perfumed chambers of the great,
> Under the canopies of costly state,
> And lull'd with sound of sweetest melody?'

Henry IV, Part II, Act iii. sc. 1, 1 4.

l. 13. *But this.* ... 'It has been the boast of some swelling moralists that every man's fortune was in his own power, that prudence supplied the place of all other divinities, and that happiness is the unfailing consequence of virtue.   But surely the quiver of Omnipotence is stored with arrows against which the shield of human virtue, however adamantine it has been boasted, is held up in vain ; we do not always suffer by our crimes ; we are not always protected by our innocence.'—Johnson, *Works*, iv. 121.

l. 15. *All natural.* ... 'I returned and saw under the sun that the race is not to the swift, nor the battle to the strong, neither yet bread to the wise, nor yet riches to men of understanding, nor yet favour to men of skill, but time and chance happeneth to them all.'—*Ecclesiastes* ix. 11.

l. 20. *All that virtue.* ... 'Locke in his last words to

Collins said :—" This world affords no solid satisfaction but the consciousness of well-doing, and the hopes of another life.'—Boswell's *Life of Johnson*, iii. 363, *n.* 3.

P. 102, l. 3. *Jerusalem.* Besieged and taken by the Emperor Titus, A. D. 70. ' This, says the historian, was the sixth time that the Jewish capital had been captured, the second time that it had been destroyed. . . . Many are the generations which have since witnessed a siege and a sack of Jerusalem.' — Merivale, *History of the Romans under the Empire*, ed. 1872, vii. 248.

l. 9. *thousands . . . .* ' Johnson talked in his usual style with a rough contempt of popular liberty. " They make a rout about *universal* liberty, without considering that all that is to be valued, or indeed can be enjoyed by individuals, is *private* liberty. Political liberty is good only so far as it produces private liberty." '—Boswell's *Life of Johnson*, ii. 60.

P. 103, l. 6. *casuists.* Johnson defines *casuist* as ' One that studies and settles cases of conscience.'

l. 21. *Where we see. . . .* This sentence, in which the princess speaks in the style of *The Rambler* is some justification for Macaulay's far too sweeping criticism—' No man,' he says, ' surely ever had so little talent for personation as Johnson.'—*Essays*, ed. 1843, i. 405. Johnson himself, in *The Rambler*, No. 20, speaking of some of his correspondents who ' affect the style and the names of ladies,' says, ' I cannot always withhold some expression of anger, like Sir Hugh in the comedy, when I happen to find that a woman has a beard.' For Sir Hugh see *The Merry Wives of Windsor*, Act iv. sc. 2.

P. 104, l. 27. *What . . .* Johnson once said :—' I believe marriages would in general be as happy, and often more so, if they were all made by the Lord Chancellor, upon a due consideration of characters and circumstances, without the parties having any choice in the matter.'—Boswell's *Life of Johnson*, ii. 461.

P. 105, l. 9. *They marry . . .* Milton, writing of the unhappiness caused by ill-sorted marriages, says :—' He who marries intends as little to conspire his own ruin as he that swears allegiance. . . . For all the wariness can be used it may yet befall a discreet man to be mistaken in his choice; and we have plenty of examples. The soberest and best-governed men are least practised in these affairs.'—Milton, *Prose Works*, Bohn's ed. iii. 176, 190.

P. 108, l. 24. *my business* . . . 'He that would travel for the entertainment of others should remember that the great object of remark is human life.'—Johnson, *The Idler*, No. 97. Pope, in the *Essay on Man*, Ep. ii. l. 2, says :—' The proper study of mankind is man.'

P. 109, l. 34. *Example* . . . ' Longum iter est per prae-cepta, breve et efficax per exempla.'—Seneca.

P. 110, l. 18. *pompous.* Johnson defines *pompous* as 'splendid, magnificent, grand.' In the *Vanity of Human Wishes*, l. 223, he has : —

　　　　' All times their scenes of pompous woes afford.'

Cf. Shakespeare's *Richard II*, Act iv. sc. 1. l. 250 :—

　　　　' To undeck the pompous body of a king.'

And Pope's *Epistle to Mr. Jervas*, l. 23 :—

　　　　' What flattering scenes our wandering fancy wrought ;
　　　　Rome's pompous glories rising to our thought !'

P. 111, l. 6. 'The whole excursion to the Pyramids from Cairo and back may be " done" in five or six hours.'—Murray's *Handbook to Egypt*, 4th ed., p. 173.

l. 20. *stepped back* . . . ' Miss Martineau says : "To the tranquil the inside of the pyramid is sufficiently airy and cool for the need of the hour. But it is a dreadful place in which to be seized with a panic, and no woman should go who cannot trust herself to put down panic by reason . . . The one danger is from the impression upon the senses of the solidity and vastness of the stone structure in such darkness." '—Murray's *Handbook*, p. 186.

l. 31. *That the dead* . . . ' Talking of ghosts, Johnson said : " It is wonderful that five thousand years have now elapsed since the creation of the world, and still it is undecided whether or not there has ever been an instance of the spirit of any person appearing after death. All argument is against it ; but all belief is for it." '—Boswell's *Life of John-*

son, iii. 230. Johnson, in his note on the ghost in *Hamlet*, speaks of it as 'an apparition which, though in all ages credited, has in all ages been considered as the most wonderful and most dreadful operation of supernatural agency.'—Johnson's *Shakespeare*, viii. 161.

P. 113, l. 5. *marble.* It is of polished granite that the grand chamber is formed.—Murray's *Handbook to Egypt*, p. 185.

l. 21. *The narrowness . . .* M. Mariette says: 'With regard to the object for which the Pyramids were destined, it is contrary to all that we know of Egypt, to all that archaeology has taught us of the monumental customs of that country, to see in them anything but tombs . . . They are the gigantic and for ever impenetrable casing of a mummy.' —Murray's *Handbook to Egypt*, p. 177. See *post*, p. 199, note on p. 153, l. 29.

l. 27. *Those who . . .* See *ante*, p. 56, l. 13.

P. 116, l. 19. *presently.* Here in the sense of 'immediately' or 'soon after.'

P. 118, l. 31. *condition. Condition*, in this sense, Johnson defines 'rank,' quoting from *The Tempest*, Act iii. sc. 1. l. 59:—

> 'I am in my condition
> A prince, Miranda.'

P. 119, l. 10. *excursions.* Johnson defines *excursion*, in this sense, as 'digression; ramble from a subject.'

l. 21. *contagion.* See *ante* p. 52, l. 34.

P. 120, l. 1. *Do not entangle . . .*

> 'Where honour or where conscience does not bind,
>   No other law shall shackle me;
>   Slave to myself I ne'er will be;
> Nor shall my future actions be confined
>   By my own present mind.'

Cowley, quoted by Johnson, *Works*, vii. 52. Johnson wrote to Mrs. Thrale : 'All unnecessary vows are folly, because they suppose a prescience of the future which has not been given us. They are, I think, a crime, because they resign that life to chance which God has given us to be regulated by reason; and superinduce a kind of fatality from which it is the great privilege of our nature to be free.'—*Piozzi Letters*, i. 83.

l. 10. *radical.* Johnson defines *radical* as '1. primitive, original; 2. implanted by nature; 3. serving to origination.' It was not till a considerable time after Johnson's death that it got the political meaning that it now bears. When the Jacobite Lord Bolingbroke, in his *Dissertation upon Parties*, Letter xviii, wrote 'Such a remedy might have wrought a radical cure of the evil that threatens our constitution,' he meant nothing more than a cure that was thorough.

l. 29. *the first night.* Cf. Blanco White's *Sonnet to Night*, which begins :—

> ' Mysterious night! when our first parent knew
> Thee from report divine, and heard thy name,
> Did he not tremble for this lovely frame,
> This glorious canopy of light and blue?'

l. 34. *But they* . . . Johnson wrote to Mrs. Thrale on the death of her husband: 'There is no wisdom in useless and hopeless sorrow; but there is something in it so like virtue, that he who is wholly without it cannot be loved, nor will by me at least be thought worthy of esteem.'—*Piozzi Letters*, ii. 198.

P. 121, l. 8. *the stream of time.* Cf. Pope, *Essay on Man*, iv. 383 :—

> ' Oh! while along the stream of time thy name
> Expanded flies, and gathers all its fame.'

l. 10. *Do not suffer* . . . Such advice as this Johnson often gave. ' Grief has its time.' ' Grief is a species of idleness.' ' Gaiety is a duty when health requires it.' ' I think business the best remedy for grief, as soon as it can be admitted. —Boswell's *Life of Johnson*, iii. 136, *n.* 2.

P. 123, l. 7. *no subject.* . . . In the vile slang of the present day it would be said, ' The price was no object.'

l. 24. *Monastery of St. Anthony.* ' After a long and painful noviciate among the tombs and in a ruined tower he [Antony] boldly advanced into the desert three days' journey to the eastward of the Nile; discovered a lonely spot which possessed the advantages of shade and water, and fixed his last residence on Mount Colzim, near the Red Sea, where an

ancient monastery still preserves the name and memory of
the saint.'—Gibbon, *Decline and Fall*, ed. 1862, iv. 307.

P. 124, l. 27. *pleasant meadow.* Johnson was thinking
of English not of Egyptian scenery.

P. 126, l. 21. *The son of Ishmael.* Cf. *Genesis* xxi. 9–21.
According to Gibbon (*Decline and Fall*, ed. 1862, vi. 206),
'The separation of the Arabs from the rest of mankind has
accustomed them to confound the ideas of stranger and
enemy ; and the poverty of the land has introduced a maxim
of jurisprudence which they believe and practise to the
present hour. They pretend that in the division of the earth
the rich and fertile climates were assigned to the other
branches of the human family ; and that the posterity of the
outlaw Ishmael might recover by fraud or force the portion
of inheritance of which he had been unjustly deprived. . . .
If a Bedoween discovers from afar a solitary traveller, he
rides furiously against him, crying with a loud voice, " Un-
dress thyself, thy aunt (*my wife*) is without a garment." A
ready submission entitles him to mercy.' See *ante*, p. 60, l. 28.

P. 127, l. 2. *Civil life. Civil*, as thus used, is defined
by Johnson, 'civilised, not barbarous.' He quotes from
Spenser :—' England was very rude and barbarous ; for it is
but even the other day since England grew civil.' He used
civility where we should now use *civilisation*, refusing to
admit *civilisation* as thus used into his *Dictionary*.—Boswell's *Life of Johnson*, ii. 155.

l. 4. *punctuality.* Johnson defines *punctuality* as 'Nicety;
scrupulous exactness.'

P. 129, l. 21. *river-horses.* In Johnson's time every
one spoke of *river-horses*; now every one speaks of *hippo-
potamuses*. This is an instance of the way in which we
injure our language by our vulgar preference of long words
derived from Greek or Latin.

P. 134, l. 29. *he was. . . .* See *ante*, p. 180, note on p. 88, l. 15.

P. 136, l. 9. *the rage of the dog-star.*

> ' Te flagrantis atrox hora Caniculae
>   Nescit tangere.'—Horace, *Odes*, iii. 13. 9.

> ' The dog-star rages.'—Pope, *Prol. to Satires*, l. 3.

l. 9. *the crab.*

> 'Aestus erat, mediusque dies ; solisque vapore
> Concava litorei fervebant brachia Cancri.'
>
> Ovid, *Metamorphoses*, x. 126.

'The Tropic Crab.'—*Paradise Lost*, x. 675.

l. 10. *elemental powers.* The powers, that is to say, of any of the four elements, usually so called, earth, fire, air and water, of which the world was thought to be composed.

P. 138, l. 1. *laws of demonstration.* Johnson said that 'a man who thinks he has seen an apparition can only be convinced himself ; his authority will not convince another, and his conviction, if rational, must be founded on being told something which cannot be known but by supernatural means.'—Boswell's *Life of Johnson*, iv. 94.

P. 139, l. 19. *Of the uncertainties . . . .* 'To Johnson, whose supreme enjoyment was the exercise of his reason, the disturbance or obscuration of that faculty was the evil most to be dreaded. Insanity, therefore, was the object of his most dismal apprehension.'—Boswell's *Life of Johnson*, i. 66. Three years before the publication of *Rasselas* Johnson wrote of the poet Collins, who had lost his reason :—'The moralists all talk of the uncertainty of fortune and the transitoriness of beauty ; but it is yet more dreadful to consider that the powers of the mind are equally liable to change, that understanding may make its appearance and depart, that it may blaze and expire.'—*Ib.* p. 276, *n.* 2.

l. 22. *The Princess was recollected.* Johnson defines *recollect* in its second sense as 'to recover reason or recollection,' and quotes from Dryden, *Aeneis*, Bk. I :—

> 'The Tyrian queen
> Admired his fortunes, more admired the man,
> Then recollected stood.'

l. 30. *Disorders of intellect . . .* That men of genius and knowledge, like the astronomer, have no certainty of a continuance of reason has been often pointed out. Burton, in his *Anatomy of Melancholy*, a book which was one of

Johnson's favourites, writes:—'You shall find that of Aristotle true, *nullum magnum ingenium sine mixtura dementiae.'*— Burton's *Anatomy of Melancholy,* ed. 1660, p. 70.

> ' Great wits are sure to madness near allied,
> And thin partitions do their bounds divide.'
> > Dryden's *Absalom and Achitophel,* l. 163.

l. 32. *Perhaps.* . . . 'For, indeed, who is not a fool, melancholy, mad ? . . . Who is not brain-sick ? Folly, melancholy, madness are but one disease ; *delirium* is a common name to all. . . . So that take melancholy in what sense you will, properly or improperly, in disposition or habit, for pleasure or for pain, dotage, discontent, fear, sorrow, madness, for part or all, truly or metaphorically, 'tis all one.'—Burton's *Anatomy,* p. 18. Johnson said, ' Many a man is mad in certain instances, and goes through life without having it perceived : for example, a madness has seized a person of supposing himself obliged literally to pray continually—had the madness turned the opposite way, and the person thought it a crime ever to pray, it might not 'mprobably have continued unobserved.'—Boswell's *Life of Johnson,* iv. 31.

P. 140, l. 5. *airy notions.* Johnson defines *airy* in this sense as ' without reality, without any steady foundation in truth or nature ; vain, trifling '; and quotes from Temple's *Miscellanies :*—' I have found a complaint concerning the scarcity of money, which occasioned many airy propositions for the remedy of it.' In *The Vanity of Human Wishes,* l. 10, he describes how man—

> ' Shuns fancied ills, or chases airy good.'

See *ante,* p. 183, note on p. 95, l. 2.

l. 8. *insanity.* *Insanity* is neither in the first edition of Johnson's *Dictionary,* which was published four years before *Rasselas,* nor in the fourth, which was the last that the author revised.

l. 29. *In time.* . . . 'Dr. Willis defined in remarkable accordance with this case in *Rasselas,* insanity to be the tendency of a mind to cherish one idea, or one set of ideas, to the exclusion of others.'—Johnson's *Works,* i. 293, note.

P. 142, l. 21. *acquaintance.* Johnson, I think, never uses the plural form *acquaintances*, though he gives it in his *Dictionary.* It is used by Bacon in *Essay* xviii., ed. 1629, i. 100.—' What acquaintances they are to seeke.' In the same Essay we find ' those of his acquaintance which are of most worth.'

P. 143, l. 12. *the changing moon.* Johnson, in writing of the repetitions in poetry and the pleasure which they often give, contemplates the moon with a very different eye. ' When night overshadows a romantic scene, all is stillness, silence, and quiet ; the poets of the grove cease their melody, the moon towers over the world in gentle majesty, men forget their labours and their cares, and every passion and pursuit is for a while suspended. All this we know already, yet we hear it repeated without weariness ; because such is generally the life of man that he is pleased to think on the time when he shall pause from a sense of his condition.'—*The Adventurer,* No. 108.

l. 13. *I have ceased.* Johnson in his old age never lost his ardent curiosity. In his sixty-ninth year he said, 'It is a man's own fault, it is from want of use, if his mind grows torpid in old age.'—Boswell's *Life of Johnson,* iii. 254.

l. 19. *Praise ...* Johnson had lost his wife before he had finished his *Dictionary.* In the Preface he says :—' I have protracted my work till most of those whom I wished to please have sunk into the grave, and success and miscarriage are empty sounds. I therefore dismiss it with frigid tranquillity, having little to fear or hope from censure or from praise.'—*Works,* v. 51. His mother was on her death-bed when he began *Rasselas,* and he had no one left to be delighted with his reputation. A few days later he wrote in *The Idler* (No. 41) :—' What is success to him that has none to enjoy it ? Happiness is not found in self-contemplation ; it is perceived only when it is reflected from another.'

P. 144, l. 9. *attained.* The old man of *Rasselas* had been already in part drawn by Johnson in the following beautiful passage in *The Vanity of Human Wishes,* the opening lines

of which he wrote, it is believed, with his mind full of his
mother :—

> ' But grant, the virtues of a temp'rate prime,
>   Bless with an age exempt from scorn or crime ;
>   An age that melts with unperceiv'd decay,
>   And glides in modest innocence away ;
>   Whose peaceful day Benevolence endears,
>   Whose night congratulating Conscience cheers ;
>   The gen'ral fav'rite as the gen'ral friend :
>   Such age there is, and who shall wish its end?
>   Yet ev'n on this her load Misfortune flings,
>   To press the weary minutes' flagging wings ;
>   New sorrow rises as the day returns,
>   A sister sickens, or a daughter mourns.
>   Now kindred Merit fills the sable bier,
>   Now lacerated Friendship claims a tear ;
>   Year chases year, decay pursues decay,
>   Still drops some joy from with'ring life away ;
>   New forms arise, and diff'rent views engage,
>   Superfluous lags the vet'ran on the stage,
>   Till pitying Nature signs the last release,
>   And bids afflicted worth retire to peace.'

l. 13. *for age* . . . Johnson was happier in his latter than
in his earlier years, as he owned to Boswell.—Boswell's *Life
of Johnson*, i. 299. Gibbon says in the close of his *Autobiography* :—'When I contemplate the common lot of mortality, I must acknowledge that I have drawn a high prize
in the lottery of life. . . . Twenty happy years have been
animated by the labour of my history, and its success has
given me a name, a rank, a character in the world, to which
I should not otherwise have been entitled. . . . I shall soon
enter into the period which, as the most agreeable of his
long life, was selected by the judgment and experience of the
sage Fontenelle. His choice is approved by the eloquent
historian of nature [Buffon], who fixes our moral happiness
to the mature season in which our passions are supposed to
be calmed, our duties fulfilled, our ambition satisfied, our
fame and fortune established on a solid basis. In private
conversation that great and amiable man added the

weight of his own experience; and this autumnal felicity
might be exemplified in the lives of Voltaire, Hume, and
many other men of letters.'—Gibbon, *Misc. Writ.*, i. 271–5.
Dr. Franklin, who was Johnson's contemporary, says in his
Autobiography :—'I should have no objection to go over the
same life from its beginning to the end.'—*Memoirs*, i. 2.
Macaulay, seven years before his death wrote :—'It is odd
that, though time is stealing from me perceptibly my vigour
and my pleasures, I am growing happier and happier. As
Milnes says, "It is shocking, it is scandalous, to enjoy life
as I do."'—Trevelyan's *Life of Lord Macaulay*, first ed., ii.
355. More than three years later he wrote :—'After fifteen
happy years passed in the Albany, I am going to leave it.'—
Ib. p. 395. Mr. Browning, in his poem of *Rabbi Ben Ezra,*
maintains the happiness of old age :—

> 'Grow old along with me!
> The best is yet to be,
> The last of life for which the first was made.
> Our times are in His hand
> Who saith, "A whole I planned,
> Youth shows but half; trust God; see all, nor be afraid." '

P. 145, l. 26. *I have. . . .* 'Without truth there must be
a dissolution of society. As it is, there is so little truth that
we are almost afraid to trust our ears; but how should we
be, if falsehood were multiplied ten times? Society is held
together by communication and information; and I remember this remark of Sir Thomas Browne's, "Do the
devils lie? No; for then hell could not subsist."'—Boswell's *Life of Johnson*, iii. 293. 'The general rule is, that
truth should never be violated, because it is of the utmost
importance to the comfort of life that we should have a
full security by mutual faith; and occasional inconveniences should be willingly suffered that we may preserve
it.'—*Ib.* iv. 305.

P. 147, l. 2. *re-collected.* 'He gathered together again.'—
Johnson, in his *Dictionary*, does not distinguish by spelling
between *re-collect* and *recollect*. See *ante*, p. 192, note on
p. 139, l. 22.

P. 148. l. 8. *I can.* . . . Johnson had drawn with great force the fate of the student in *The Vanity of Human Wishes*, l. 143 :—

> ' Yet, should thy soul indulge the gen'rous heat
>   Till captive Science yields her last retreat ;
>   Should Reason guide thee with her brightest ray,
>   And pour on misty Doubt resistless day ;
>   Should no false kindness lure to loose delight,
>   Nor praise relax, nor difficulty fright ;
>   Should tempting Novelty thy cell refrain,
>   And Sloth effuse her opiate fumes in vain ;
>   Should Beauty blunt on fops her fatal dart,
>   Nor claim the triumph of a letter'd heart ;
>   Should no disease thy torpid veins invade,
>   Nor Melancholy's phantoms haunt thy shade ;
>   Yet hope not life from grief or danger free,
>   Nor think the doom of man revers'd for thee.'

l. 9. *in the attainment* . . . ' The great praise of Socrates is, that he drew the wits of Greece by his instruction and example from the vain pursuit of natural philosophy to moral inquiries, and turned their thoughts from stars and tides, and matter and motion, upon the various modes of virtue and relations of life.'—*The Rambler*, No. 24.

l. 16. *scrupulosity.* See *ante*, p. 185, note on p. 98, l. 2.

P. 149, l. 27. *but when* . . . ' The greatest burden in the world is superstition, not only of ceremonies in the church, but of imaginary and scarecrow sins at home.'—Milton, *Prose Works*, Bohn's ed., iii. 176.

P. 150, l. 3. *scruples.* Johnson defines *scruple* as *doubt; difficulty of determination; perplexity; generally about minute things.* His writings and sayings contain such passages as the following :—' I am afraid of scruples.' ' Let me warn you very earnestly against scruples.' ' Scruples made many men miserable, but few men good.'—Boswell's *Life of Johnson*, ii. 421.

l. 5. *fly to business.* . . . Burton, in the last lines of *The Anatomy of Melancholy*, says :—' Only take this for a coral-lary and conclusion ; as thou tenderest thine own welfare in this and all other melancholy, thy good health of body and mind, observe this short precept, give not way to solitariness and idleness. "Be not solitary, be not idle."'

P. 151, l. 11. *Those men.*... 'Je n'ai que vingt arpents répondit le Turc ; je les cultive avec mes enfants ; le travail éloigne de nous trois grands maux, l'ennui, le vice, et le besoin ... Je sais aussi, dit Candide, qu'il faut cultiver notre jardin. Vous avez raison, dit Pangloss ; car, quand l'homme fut mis dans le jardin d'Éden, il y fut mis *ut operaretur eum*, pour qu'il travaillât ; ce qui prouve que l'homme n'est pas né pour le repos. Travaillons sans raisonner, dit Martin c'est le seul moyen de rendre la vie supportable.'—*Candide*, ch. xxx.

l. 18. *Their time* ... It was, no doubt, the conviction that it is in occupation that happiness is most surely found that led Johnson often 'to observe, that it was the greatest misfortune which could befall a man to have been bred to no profession, and pathetically to regret that this misfortune was his own.'—Boswell's *Life of Johnson*, iii. 309, *n.* 1.

P. 152, l. 6. *little strength* ... 'I do not wonder,' wrote Johnson, 'that, where the monastic life is permitted, every order finds votaries, and every monastery inhabitants. Men will submit to any rule by which they may be exempted from the tyranny of caprice and of chance. They are glad to supply by external authority their own want of constancy and resolution, and court the government of others, when long experience has convinced them of their own inability to govern themselves.'—Boswell's *Life of Johnson*, i. 365. See *ante*, p. 180, note on p. 89, l. 27.

l. 19. *die in a crowd.* 'He then in a low and earnest tone talked of his meditating upon the awful hour of his own dissolution, and in what manner he should conduct himself upon that occasion. "I know not," said he, "whether I should wish to have a friend by me, or have it all between God and myself."'—Boswell's *Life of Johnson*, ii. 93. Macaulay wrote :—'For my part, I feel that I should die best in the situation of Charles the First, or Lewis the Sixteenth, or Montrose ;—I mean quite alone, surrounded

by enemies, and nobody that I cared for near me.'—
Trevelyan's *Life of Lord Macaulay*, first ed., ii. 354.

l. 20. *harmless pleasure.* Johnson, in his eulogy on Garrick
in the *Lives of the Poets* (*Works*, vii. 380), said that 'his
death impoverished the public stock of harmless pleasure.'
Boswell 'objected, "Is not *harmless pleasure* very tame?"
JOHNSON: "Nay, Sir, harmless pleasure is the highest praise.
Pleasure is a word of dubious import; pleasure is in general
dangerous and pernicious to virtue; to be able therefore to
furnish pleasure that is harmless, pleasure pure and unalloyed, is as great a power as man can possess." '—Boswell's
Life of Johnson, iii. 388.

l. 24. *image.* See *ante*, p. 176, note on p. 80, l. 26.

l. 29. *Mortification* . . . 'Austerities and mortifications
are means by which the mind is invigorated and roused, by
which the attractions of pleasure are interrupted, and the
chains of sensuality are broken. . . . Austerity is the proper
antidote to indulgence; the diseases of mind as well as body
are cured by contraries.'—*The Rambler*, No. 110.

P. 153, l. 12. *I know not* . . . Johnson himself would
not have gone into the Catacombs. Boswell tells how, at
an old ruinous chapel in the Hebrides, where some human
bones were exposed, 'he started back from them with a
striking appearance of horror.'—Boswell's *Life of Johnson*,
v. 169.

l. 29. *What reason* . . . 'The inviolate preservation of the
body was deemed essential to the corporeal resurrection of
the "justified" dead. The living man consisted of a body,
a soul, an intelligence, and an appearance or *eidolon*—in
Egyptian, a *ka*. Death dissociated these four parts, which
must ultimately be reunited for all eternity. Between death
on earth and life everlasting there intervened, however, a
period varying from 3000 to 10,000 years, during which the
intelligence wandered, luminous, through space, while the
soul performed a painful probationary pilgrimage through
the mysterious under-world. The body, in order that it
should await intact the return of the soul whose habitation
it was, must meanwhile be guarded from corruption and

every danger. Hence, and hence only, the extraordinary measures taken to ensure the preservation of the corpse and the inviolability of the sepulchre; hence the huge pyramid, the secret pit, and the subterraneous labyrinth. The shadowy and impalpable *ka* was supposed to dwell in the tomb with the mummied body. This fragile [*sic*] conception was not, however, indestructible, like the soul and the intelligence. Being an aspect, it must perforce be the aspect of something material; and if the body which it represented were destroyed or damaged, the *ka* was liable to the like mischance. In view of this danger, the Egyptian, by stocking his sepulchre with portrait statues, sought to provide the *ka* with other chances of continuance.... As many as twenty duplicates have been found in a single tomb, and always secreted in hidden chambers constructed in the thickness of the walls of the sepulchre.'—*Encycl. Brit.*, ninth ed., xvii. 20.

P. 154, l. 13. *I suppose*... Herodotus describes three modes of embalming, varying in costliness, the cheapest of which is practised in the case of the poorer classes. He does not mention any other mode of burial. (Bk. ii. ch. 86-88.) In the *Encycl. Brit.*, ninth ed., xvii. 21, it is stated: 'According to the religious law of ancient Egypt the rites of mummification were universal and compulsory, being performed, not only for every native in a style consistent with his rank in life, but also for all strangers and foreigners who died in the land, for all slaves and captives, and even for outcasts, criminals, and lepers.'

l. 29. *Some*... 'Metaphysical topics suppose that the soul is immaterial, and that it is impossible for thought to belong to a material substance. But just metaphysics teach us that the notion of substance is wholly confused and imperfect; and that we have no other idea of any substance than as an aggregate of particular qualities inhering in an unknown something. Matter therefore and spirit are at bottom equally unknown; and we cannot determine what qualities inhere in the one or in the other. They likewise teach us, that nothing can be decided *a priori* concerning any cause or effect; and that experience being the only source of our judgments of this nature we cannot know from any other principle whether matter by its structure or arrangement may not be the cause of thought.'—Hume's *Phil. Works*, ed. 1854, iv. 547.

P. 156, l. 20. *idea.* Johnson defines *idea* as 'mental imagination.' Boswell says that ' Johnson was at all times jealous of infractions upon the genuine English language. . . . He was particularly indignant against the almost universal use of the word *idea* in the sense of *notion* or *opinion*, when it is clear that *idea* can only signify something of which an image can be formed in the mind.'—Boswell's *Life of Johnson*, iii. 196.

l. 23. *indiscerptible.* Johnson defines *indiscerptible* as ' incapable of being broken or destroyed by dissolution of parts.' Under *discerptible* he quotes from More's *Div. Dialogues*:—' Matter is moveable, this immoveable ; matter discerptible, this indiscerptible.'

l. 29. *That it will* . . . Plato, in the tenth book of the *Republic*, maintains that ' all things have their own corrupting element ; and if this does not destroy them nothing else will. And the soul has her own corrupting principles, which are injustice, intemperance, cowardice, and the like. But none of these destroy the soul in the same sense that disease destroys the body. The soul may be full of all iniquities, but is not by reason of them all brought any nearer to death. . . . If the natural inherent evil of the soul be unable to destroy the soul, hardly will anything else destroy her. But the soul which cannot be destroyed either by internal or external evil must endure for ever, and, lasting for ever, must be immortal.'—Jowett's *Dialogues of Plato*, 2nd ed., iii. 133.

l. 33. *higher authority* . . . Hume, in like manner, concludes his *Essay on the Immortality of the Soul* by saying : ' Nothing could set in a fuller light the infinite obligations which mankind have to Divine revelation, since we find that no other medium could ascertain this great and important truth.'—Hume's *Phil. Works*, ed. 1854, iv. 555.

l. 34. *collected.* Johnson defines *to collect himself*, ' to recover from surprise ; to gain command over his thoughts ; to assemble his sentiments,' quoting from *The Tempest*, Act i. sc. 2 :

> ' Be collected ;
> No more amazement.'

P. 157, l. 9. *To me* . . . With this saying of the Princess, which may be looked upon as ' the conclusion of the whole matter,' it is interesting to compare the last lines of *The Vanity of Human Wishes* :—

> ' Where then shall Hope and Fear their objects find ?
> Must dull Suspense corrupt the stagnant mind ?
> Must helpless man in ignorance sedate.
> Roll darkling down the torrent of his fate ?
> Must no dislike alarm, no wishes rise,
> No cries invoke the mercies of the skies ?
> Inquirer, cease ; petitions yet remain
> Which Heaven may hear, nor deem Religion vain.
> Still raise for good the supplicating voice,
> But leave to Heaven the measure and the choice.
> Safe in his power, whose eyes discern afar
> The secret ambush of a specious prayer ;
> Implore his aid, in his decisions rest,
> Secure, whate'er he gives, he gives the best.
> Yet, when the sense of sacred presence fires,
> And strong devotion to the skies aspires,
> Pour forth thy fervours for a healthful mind,
> Obedient passions, and a will resign'd ;
> For love, which scarce collective man can fill ;
> For patience, sov'reign o'er transmuted ill ;
> For faith, that, panting for a happier seat,
> Counts death kind Nature's signal of retreat :
> These goods for man the laws of Heaven ordain,
> These goods he grants, who grants the power to gain ,
> With these celestial Wisdom calms the mind.
> And makes the happiness she does not find.'

P. 158, l. 1. *The princess* . . . Lord Tennyson's poem, *The Princess*, might have been suggested by this passage. The old King, her father, says of her :

'Knowledge, so my daughter held,
Was all in all . . . . .
. . . At last she begged a boon,
A certain summer-palace which I have
Hard by your father's frontier : I said no,
Yet being an easy man, gave it ; and there,
All wild to found an University
For maidens, on the spur she fled.'

Seventh ed., p. 22.

l. 7. *prudence.* Johnson defines *prudence* as 'wisdom applied to practice.'

THE END

PRINTED IN
GREAT BRITAIN
AT THE
UNIVERSITY PRESS
OXFORD
BY
CHARLES BATEY
PRINTER
TO THE
UNIVERSITY